LEGACY

The Hemophilia of Yesterday

Insights on Life with Hemophilia
From the Journals of Ralph Dean Rytting
The War Years, 1942–1944

LEGACY

The Hemophilia of Yesterday

Matthew Dean Barkdull

Note that the content, spelling, and grammar of the journal entries cited in this book have not been altered from the original.

Printed in the United States of America.

Publishing services provided by Scrivener Books.
ScrivenerBooks.com
info@scrivenerbooks.com

ISBN 978-0-9895523-4-9

To my grandfather, Ralph Dean Rytting, an inspiration and light through my discouraging days of adversity. May this book be a monument to his rich life.

And to those who have left their own legacies, may we build upon your firm foundations.

Matthew Barkdull
August 2014

RALPH DEAN RYTTING, 1926–1971

Ralph in the hospital, surrounded by his beloved music and typewriter

Ralph Dean Rytting was born on October 22, 1926, in the rural community of Shelley, Idaho. Although Ralph was born with severe factor IX deficiency, also known as hemophilia B, his condition was not diagnosed until age sixteen at the Mayo Clinic in Rochester, Minnesota. Ralph seldom attended public school because of his health problems, yet he had a passion for learning. A voracious reader and writer, Ralph was both home-tutored and self-educated. He married Georgia Collins in 1948 and had two children, Colby and Elizabeth. Ralph and Georgia sang and toured with the Mormon Tabernacle Choir for most of their married lives. Ralph was president of his own audio consulting business, Ralph Rytting Audio, Inc. He was a strong advocate for hemophilia research, and was interested in new advances in managing this disorder. In his lifetime, Ralph had more than 3,500 blood transfusions. He died unexpectedly in his sleep on March 25, 1971, at age forty-four.

CONTENTS

FOREWORD

AMERICAN AUTHOR G. K. Chesterton wrote, "Brave men are all vertebrates; they have their softness on the surface and their toughness in the middle." Ralph Rytting was such a man: his introspective, gentle and sensitive side was revealed in his exquisite journal entries from the 1940s, when he was a young man coming of age in Idaho. Ralph's steely inner core helped him endure the pain of hemophilia—just as soldiers endured the pain of injuries on the battlefields of Europe. Yet he never allowed his difficult lot in life to embitter his feelings; his surface never became as tough as his core. Instead, Ralph maintained a sensitivity that heightened his awareness of others' feelings and sufferings, sharpened his observations of nature, and deepened his appreciation of the simplest pleasures in life.

To read Ralph's journals is to be surprised—at his youth, the wisdom of his words, the depth of his feelings. Like an archeologist searching for artifacts from ancient civilizations and finding uncanny similarity to contemporary customs, I see Ralph's strength, courage and empathy in men who live with hemophilia today. They know the agony of bleeds and face the challenge of being different. How beautifully Ralph expressed these timeless thoughts and feelings.

I was especially struck by Ralph's journals because I am also an avid journal writer. I've kept journals periodically since I was ten. My early efforts are long gone, unfortunately. But today I write in a journal I began in February 1987, on the day I learned that I was pregnant with my first child, my son Tommy. In this journal I poured out my joys, hopes and fears while pregnant. I wrote about the day Tommy was born and later about the mysterious bleeding that plagued him. When he was two months old, we learned that Tommy had hemophilia and this diagnosis changed my life forever. I became a professional writer and educator about hemophilia.

I hope my journals become my legacy to my children. And I hope my hemophilia books are my legacy to a community that always needs education and needs to educate others. Ralph's journal is his legacy, left to his family and now shared with our community.

As I read Ralph's journal, the word courage came repeatedly to mind. Whether you're a person with hemophilia or the parent of a child with hemophilia, may this book strengthen your courage, offer comfort, and instill optimism. I hope you'll find great inspiration in the words of this brave young man—tender on the outside, tough on the inside—and his resilient spirit despite life's unpredictable challenges.

Laurie Kelley
Boston, Massachusetts
September 2006

PREFACE

FROM 1939 TO 1945, the world was engaged in the life-and-death struggle of World War II. In the remote farming town of Idaho Falls, Idaho, another war was raging: a war against the ravages of hemophilia. This book is a snapshot of the teenage years of my grandfather, Ralph Dean Rytting, who had hemophilia B and fought his own unique war. Ralph's journal entries cover the years from 1942 to 1944, when he was fifteen to seventeen years old. Ralph's war with hemophilia was relentless and isolating. No one else in Ralph's family had hemophilia. At that time, treatment for the disorder was primitive. Doctors relied mainly on whole blood transfusions to stop bleeding. Medical knowledge was limited: aspirin (also called anicin or "pain capsules") was often prescribed to relieve the horrendous pain of hemophilia bleeds. Today, we know that aspirin actually thins the blood and can cause excess bleeding. When Ralph was a teenager, experimental techniques, such as injecting snake venom, offered desperate hemophilia sufferers the unlikely hope of stopping a hemorrhage. That Ralph survived both traditional and experimental treatments is nothing short of a miracle.

Like Ralph, I have hemophilia. After reading his personal journals, I decided to write a book about the legacy of the man from whom I inherited my disorder. Originally intending this project for a small audience—my family—I began researching and interviewing the people who knew Ralph best. As I explored Ralph's diaries, feasting on reminiscences, photographs, memoirs and letters, I began to see hemophilia in a new light:

I realized that my grandfather's hemophilia and mine are like two different disorders. Medically, my hemophilia is no different than Ralph's. We both lack the blood protein factor IX, needed to clot our blood. But today's treatment options are so advanced that the difference between my quality of life and Ralph's is immeasurable. From the 1920s through the 1940s, Ralph's generation knew little about hemophilia, and treatments were crude at best. As I read of Ralph's struggles and the days that taxed and stretched his stamina as he endured endless hemorrhages, I came to know this good man. The more I learned, the more amazed I was to discover that my own feelings about hemophilia lightened. I complied more with factor infusions and complained less. I recognized and appreciated the freedom I enjoy as a result of modern treatments.

Contemplating my changing attitude toward hemophilia, I envisioned Ralph's story affecting a larger audience than just my family. All people with bleeding disorders, their families, and their caregivers can appreciate his journals. Ralph's life can become a historical marker in the bleeding disorder community, promoting healing, learning, and happy living. Ralph offers us a sense of hope: the knowledge that we can all face and overcome the challenges of bleeding disorders. As Ralph fought his battle with hemophilia, he had the courage and strength to become a contributing member of his community, dedicated friend, father and husband, president of his own business, and member of the Mormon Tabernacle Choir. His story helps us value the research, support, networking, treatment, prevention, and knowledge we enjoy today—things that Ralph didn't have. I hope this book will become a legacy for future pioneers who will chart the rugged terrain of experimentation and medical breakthrough so that we can all experience a better quality of life.

This book is divided into two parts. Part 1 details Ralph's sufferings with hemophilia, a condition that was not diagnosed until April 30, 1943 when he was sixteen. Ralph's journal entries express his aspirations, discouragements, and confusion about his condition until he received a correct diagnosis. In Part 2, Ralph guides us through his life, his loves, and his philosophy. Between Parts 1 and 2 is Miracle at Sea, written by Ralph's wife, Georgia, who recounts Ralph's amazing experience during an ocean voyage in 1955. Throughout, I have quoted Ralph's entries with minimal editing to illustrate his engaging personality, his routines, his dreams and frustrations, and his suffering.

May Ralph's story link us more closely to those early pioneers who suffered with hemophilia and to those who developed successful treatments. May our present challenges continue to lighten, thanks to advanced treatment, as we rise above endurance and enjoy active living. May we create personal legacies that inspire future generations to appreciate the quality of life they have and to continue improving life for their children.

INTRODUCTION

June 1942, Idaho Falls

It is an evening in late June, and the sun is still up, though just now being hidden behind a dirty, flaxen cloud that hangs above a row of trees west of where I am sitting. A slight breeze rustles by irregularly, disturbing bushes and trees, and now and then blowing a strand of hair down over my eyes, greatly aggravating me, since I do need a haircut, and my arm gets tired from sweeping it back. A few solitary comae [tufts of hairs attached to the hard outer covering of a seed] are floating along with the breeze, coming from the tall cottonwoods behind our house and out of my sight.

The sun has appeared again from behind the cloud, momentarily blinding me, only to disappear behind another [cloud].

Wisps of brownish smoke arise from the tall chimney of a yellow brick house separated from me by a graveled road, and not more than 100 feet away, and drag along the ground to become slowly and subtly absorbed into the fresh, cool atmosphere.

A chill comes into the air, and I shiver slightly; but it is quick in passing, and only serves to make the coming appearance of an undecided sun more inviting.

How green and virile everything appears! brought on by a late and stormy spring and tempestuous summer.

The clouds above me are a dirty greyish mass of sifting vapor, bordered by bright white, through whose translucent contents a luminous orbit betrays the presence of a hiding sun.

A black '39 Plymouth just turned the corner by our house and stirred up a long, endless cloud of dust that settles o'er our lawn and does much to dull its virility.

Ralph Dean Rytting, age 15

It had been a long day. Work had been particularly arduous and the last thing I wanted that evening was to infuse myself with factor. I finally relented to my dutiful wife and went to the refrigerator where the factor takes up most of the space.

What a drag! I quickly mixed the factor and, at my customary spot at the kitchen table, prepared my scarred hands for infusion. I jabbed the needle into a quivering vein and a line of blood filled the narrow tube extending from the butterfly needle. Success. Just as I started thinking about weightier matters, I noticed my hand swelling up near the needle's entry point. Infiltrated! Biting my lip, I removed the needle and cursed my luck.

Tired but determined, I scoped out another vein to victimize. Once again, I inserted the needle and blood filled the tube. But the moment I began pushing in the factor concentrate, an unwelcome ballooning again appeared under my skin. To blow off steam, I gave my vein an unprintable lecture. I wish I could say that fate was kind but two more attempts yielded similar results. Near tears, I wanted to throw the medicine against the wall but, at $3,000 a shot, that decision would be financially unwise.

Why is this happening to me? Why do I deserve this? I'm tired—Let me go to sleep! Emotionally, I wasn't in a good position to deal with uncooperative veins. But, fortunately, the planets eventually aligned and the next attempt succeeded. Slowly pushing in the factor, I glanced down at my hands, the unwilling targets of what looked like an acupuncture frenzy. I shifted my gaze to the mess of boxes, alcohol wipes, and needles on the table. Thoughtfully, I watched the syringe with the clear liquid being dispensed into my waiting vein. Words from the past—Grandpa's words—shot through me like lightning, humbling me and giving me precious perspective.

Wednesday, January 27, 1943

I surely hope this new idea of mine for this kind of diary works out satisfactorily, and that I can keep on making excerpts. And say what I think and feel, not just what is ordinarily said in speaking to other people. As long as my health lasts, I intend to make an entry at least every two days, and once a day if possible.

Oh, if my health only does hold up! I hope I can go back to the Mayo Clinic soon and find out what my trouble is, if possible, and if there is a chance of it being cured; and also if it is possible that this is a hereditary disease that might be passed on. That worries me more than anything, for I do so want to be able to raise a good, healthy family. More and more lately, I am thinking in terms of marriage and vocational training, and the responsibilities that must come sooner or later. I do hope that I can prove capable of taking on a vocation and getting married, though of course not for years yet.

Friday, April 2, 1943

It has been another very dull day. Of late I have accomplished so little and done so few things that it is pitiful. If only my health holds up and I recover completely from this darned ear! There are so many things that

I wish to do. First, get on with my schoolwork; second, get some more writing done; third, engage in more social activities and establish more social contacts. And none of these can I do when I am sick—or the doing of them is greatly handicapped, if not made impossible.

Ralph Dean Rytting, age 16

My eyes moistened as I remembered these words of hope, concern, initiative, and courage. They were the words of my grandfather: a boy, then, with values, dreams, and aspirations. A boy who faced repeated predictions of death from an illness that baffled both his family and his doctors. In reflection, and with a measure of guilt, I looked down at the syringe that contained the precious factor concentrate, a simple-looking medication, clear as water and valuable as gold—the medicine that I had cursed for interfering with my sleep schedule.

What a fool I am! What my grandfather would have given for this medication! Ralph Dean Rytting was born at a time when science hadn't yet discovered how to separate the missing clotting protein from whole blood and then freeze-dry and bottle it. Only in the mid-1960s did factor concentrate become available commercially. The introduction of factor concentrate allowed people with hemophilia to treat themselves intravenously in minutes at home or at work. Factor concentrate freed thousands of people from crippling bleeds and prolonged hospital visits.

Unfortunately, my grandfather Ralph couldn't take advantage of this drug for most of his life. In 1971, a mourner at Ralph's funeral gave this thought-provoking statement:

Those of you who have had children, put yourself in the position of these fine parents. They have had two fine daughters in the family and then along comes the long awaited son: a beautiful boy, a splendid son. Happiness and elation fills this fine and united family.

Then as this little toddler begins to lose his teeth, they find bleeding. As this little fellow stumbles and falls and skins his knee, it doesn't heal. As he learns to ride his trike and falls, he sprains his wrist and a month or two passes before this can be useful. And then the inevitable truth comes out: "We have a son with a dreaded disease of hemophilia." He's a bleeder. There is no known cure. Panic, frustration, and grief is beginning to grip the hearts of this family and the parents. The inevitable search for a cure: "something we can do to alleviate the suffering and the pain of this boy of ours. Surely there is a way to find a cure for this disease." Trials are made with unproven methods. Creosote, an oily preservative distilled from tar, is administered to the blood to try to find a coagulant that would calm and cease the bleeding of this young man. Snake venom was introduced into his body, hoping that this would cause a coagulation of the blood. Trips are made to the Mayo Clinic. Money is poured out. The sacrifice of an automobile is made. "We can't afford an automobile. We must take care of this boy! We must find a cure!" The endless search goes on and on and on. Frustration, some small successes, hopes, and then tragedy again. Hours and days and weeks and months on end are spent in bed recuperating, always recuperating. He can't attend school. His friends come by. He's tutored, he learns from books, he becomes an avid reader, an avid student. He becomes brilliant in his mind, he becomes self-taught. This has been the life of Ralph Rytting up to this point.

The illness that now simply delayed my sleep had once threatened my grandfather's life and livelihood. Sleep was not on Ralph's mind when he wrote his journal entries. The ability to live and raise a family, secure a job, and have a social life were the burning issues that haunted him. I imagined that, unlike me, he would gladly have stayed up all night and endured temporary inconvenience if he knew he could be well for the foreseeable future.

Lost in these thoughts, I gazed at the syringe. The concentrate was gone, a single air bubble marking the end of this infusion cycle. I was finished and would go to bed shortly, confident that I was now protected against any spontaneous bleeding. I looked down at the scattered medical supplies on the kitchen table. It was late and tomorrow was another workday. I would awake to fulfill my responsibilities and provide a living for my family. I smiled. Humbly, I whispered my quiet thanks to a man I had never known but whom I loved for giving me perspective that evening. I fell asleep with respect in my heart for the legacy of Ralph Dean Rytting.

PART ONE

The Crucible of Hemophilia

Ralph once leveled with me on how difficult the pain could get. Compare your own experience of a headache, he said, and then imagine your worst headache all over. Then imagine it going deeper—not simply to the bone, but into the very center. That's the kind of pain that he had when he bled internally. About 3,500 blood transfusions. He told me that he had tried drugs to a point. He told me that he had developed a technique of self-hypnosis that helped him some. He told me that there was a level, however, where none of those was any help at all. That's particularly when the hydraulic pressure in his hip became unbearable.

—Truman Madsen, friend of Ralph Rytting

Ralph Dean Rytting, age 10

CHAPTER 1

The Healing Power of the Past

He who loses wealth loses much;
He who loses a friend loses more;
But he that loses his courage loses all.

—Miguel De Cervantes

All parents of children with a bleeding disorder can remember in detail the day they heard the diagnosis. Shock is often their first reaction, then reflection, and re-evaluation of priorities. For a time, emotion outweighs objectivity as parents try to come to grips with news that has far-reaching effects. Chronic illness—the term can sound like a death sentence. The days and weeks following the diagnosis are spent searching for answers and dealing with the unknown.

A husband and wife I've known for years were blessed with a healthy boy and excited to discover they were expecting a girl. Happily, they started shopping for clothes, preparing the nursery, and stocking up on supplies. They dreamed of what life would be like: cheering her softball games, watching her dance at ballet recitals, chasing away boys, expressing their love when she married, and enjoying their grandchildren when she became a mother. The day of her birth arrived, and the little girl was born with Down syndrome. The husband and wife were devastated. They loved their child dearly but they grieved for their own lost dreams. Now they had to adjust and tailor life to a set of conditions about which they had little prior knowledge and no experience. This process of emotional healing takes time. But how do we learn to cope with such difficult challenges?

An appreciation of the past is one road to improving our ability to cope. As we consider other people's stories, particularly those from the past, an interesting process begins. We gain perspective about the way our present circumstance fits into the long line of human experience. And we emerge better equipped to face our own trials. Our society honors and celebrates the past. We erect historical markers to remind us of past events and people. We are inspired by heroism; we revere extraordinary acts of courage. We remember because in the remembering we find ourselves. As Rudyard Kipling says,

The tumult and the shouting dies;
The captains and the kings depart.
Still stands thine ancient sacrifice,
An humble and a contrite heart.
Lord God of Hosts, be with us yet,
Lest we forget, lest we forget.[1]

We must keep the light of the past burning, "Lest we forget, lest we forget."

I recently visited two hospitals in Salt Lake City, Utah for my annual hemophilia checkup: Primary Children's Medical Center and the University of Utah Hospital. I affectionately call this my "Blood and Guts Checkup". I had appointments with the hematologist for my hemophilia, the hepatologist for my hepatitis C, and the nephrologist for the kidney transplant I had in 1990. Normally, I try to be good-spirited about these

---

[1] Kipling, Rudyard, "Recessional," 1897.

visits, but this day I was surprised at how negative I felt about having to go to the hospital … again. I felt sorry for myself—a perpetually sick person who can't achieve equilibrium without medication. In fact, I thought, medication is keeping me alive. I thought about my wife and three children, and their uncertain future with me as husband and father. I felt very down.

As I sat near the main entrance of Primary Children's Medical Center, nibbling on a dry sandwich, bemoaning my condition and gazing sadly at a fountain in the foyer, I began to notice the young patients parading before me with their parents. The gravity of their ailments surprised me. These small, innocent children wore casts, tubes, IVs, masks, and restraints. Watching them, I couldn't help feeling tearful. My tears weren't triggered by their illnesses but by their attitudes. These children had every right to be miserable, but they were not—and neither were their parents. Here were people who loved each other. I watched parents lifting up feeble children to show them the fountain, in a brief but valued moment of relief from the daily regimen of discomfort. I saw balloons tied to little wagons for children who could not sit up; I observed parents patiently adjusting little bodies so they could be comfortable. All these acts of kindness were done with smiles, hugs, and laughter. I was inspired. During that precious lunch hour before my clinics began, I was the student and these children and parents were my instructors. They taught me about perspective, fortitude, love, and appreciation. My own troubles faded. I gained a new attitude about my clinical visits.

That day, the incredible strength of those families was seared on my soul, and I have thought of the children and their parents again and again. Somehow, as I sat by that fountain, Ralph's story had helped me really see those families. They shared Ralph's qualities: perseverance, love, and hope.

Idaho Falls, circa 1942

It was a lovely afternoon: warm, clear, clean and fresh. I walked outside for a moment, and just stood there and enjoyed it. It was so warm that I opened the front door and the light came in brightly, painting a silhouette on the kitchen door. It is too bad that things are so ephemeral—that they are never lasting, that everything is over with for eternity the minute it is done. That memories will continue to be nothing but memories, that vivid scenes will grow less vivid, and recollections of beauty—a gorgeous view, a friend, a performance or occasion—will die away gradually, will never be refreshened by their re-occurrence. And yet, would it be good if everything were repeated, if time did not move on? No, I know it would not … and yet, it still does give you a funny feeling sometimes to think about these things.

Ralph Dean Rytting, age 15

CHAPTER 2

A Young Man's Plight

You must carry a chaos inside you
to give birth to a dancing star.

—Friedrich Nietzsche

THE DAY WAS AUGUST 12, 1904. The cannons at St. Petersburg's Fortress of Peter and Paul thundered a salute three hundred times. Almost immediately, Russia was a symphony of church bells, heralding the news: The Tsarevich, His Imperial Highness Alexis Nicolaevich Romanov, heir to the Russian throne, had been born to Nicholas II and Alexandra, Tsar and Empress of Russia. In the midst of this jubilation across Nicholas' vast expanse of terrain, no one suspected that Alexis had a bleeding disorder. He had inherited hemophilia from his mother, a granddaughter of Queen Victoria of England. At the time, Queen Victoria was the most famous carrier of hemophilia, which was later dubbed the "royal disease." Young Alexis would be diagnosed shortly after birth, and would eventually be considered the most famous person with hemophilia in history, a distinction that no soul would envy.

The young Tsarevich was born as a revolution was developing in Russia. Vladimir Lenin and his disciples would eventually stir millions to revolt against the monarchy, and establish communist rule in the Revolution of 1917. Alexis' hemophilia contributed indirectly to the revolt as the young Tsarevich's horrific suffering constantly distracted his parents. In desperation, Nicholas and

Alexandra turned to Rasputin, a corrupt monk who appeared to lessen Alexis' pain with his unusual hypnotic techniques. Considered a savior by the royal parents, Rasputin was a pariah to the Russian people: a man who used the royal family and hemophilia to gain political power. Distracted by hemophilia, struggling in World War I, and facing mounting criticism by their people, the Russian royal family was eventually assassinated by the Communists who seized power.

Twenty-two years after Alexis' birth, on October 22, 1926, another boy with hemophilia was born. In the small town of Shelley, Idaho, Rudolph and Phoebe Rytting welcomed their infant son, Ralph. Ralph's birth wasn't accompanied by church bells, cannons, or gun salutes. Yet as this humble couple looked with pride at their first son, they considered themselves richer than monarchs.

Alexis was born into a chaotic world; at Ralph's birth, the world was equally chaotic. Fear and uncertainty reigned. The Great Depression was only three years away. The stock market would crash on October 24, 1929, causing high unemployment, despair, and suffering. The world was recovering from World War I, the war that devastated Russia and ended the Romanov rule. Now, Hitler's dreams of dominance took root as he began to reorganize his Nazi Party which would plunge the world into unparalleled conflict. Despite the hardships that would challenge the Rytting family as a result of world conditions, this family of five looked with hope to the future. After the birth of daughters Lucie and Alta, the Ryttings, like the Romanovs, had their first boy. But unlike the Romanovs, the Ryttings would have to wait sixteen years to discover the illness that plagued their son. Gazing at Ralph, the horizon seemed bright.

Yet some commonality existed between Alexis and Ralph: two boys born with severe hemophilia and two sets of parents struggling for years to assuage the pain of intense, unrelenting hemorrhages. In Ralph's time, as in Alexis' time, neither parents nor doctors could do much. Robert K. Massie[2] gives a chilling but accurate assessment of the pain endured by Alexis and witnessed by Alexis' mother, Alexandra:

> *Because [Alexandra] had waited so long and prayed so hard for her son, the revelation that Alexis suffered from hemophilia struck Alexandra with savage force. From that moment, she lived in the particular sunless world reserved for the mothers of hemophiliacs. For any woman, there is no more exquisite torture than watching helplessly as a beloved child suffers in extreme pain. Alexis, like every other child, looked to his mother for protection. When he hemorrhaged into a joint and the pounding pain obliterated everything else from his consciousness, he still was able to cry, 'Mama, help me, help me!' For Alexandra sitting beside him, unable to help, each cry seemed a sword thrust into the bottom of her heart.*

A sunless world—an accurate description of the place where parents go when faced with a frightening prognosis for a chronically ill child. Rudolph and Phoebe Rytting entered this sunless place when, time after time, they watched little Ralph battle an undiagnosed ailment that tortured his body … with no way to help.

Despite the constant worry and fear that must have gripped Rudolph and Phoebe, they insisted that Ralph live his life fully even if that meant suffering. Because of Ralph's active lifestyle, his bleeding episodes took on a predictable cycle: hemorrhages

---

[2] Massie, Robert K., *Nicholas and Alexandra.* New York: Ballantine Books, 1995.

would come and go, moments of health would be treasured, and invigoration would follow. Ralph would feel obliged to "catch up" by engaging in risky activities. He would notice a joint stiffening and soon be unable to move it. Then came the crucible: non-abating, hammering pain that racked his joints for days and nights—profound bleeding into joints until the intense pressure of the pooled blood would clamp blood vessels and bring a halt to the hemorrhage. Pianist and conductor Ardean Watts, Ralph's lifelong friend, described this drama:

> *Things would build up with Ralph, and if there was a good dance going on, he would go and all of us knew that he would dance too much and that he would probably be in bed for a few weeks as a result. But that didn't deter him in the least. He took the risks, paid the price and, very frequently, if we knew he was going out on a big date, we would listen for the ambulance to come in the middle of the night. When he got home, the ambulance would pick him up and take him to the hospital. That would be anything from an overnight visit to several weeks. When it extended to several weeks, then we would go up to the hospital and "hold court." He took full advantage! There was always a bevy of nurses who sensed the fact that he was different. But, for the very high-class ladies, he was very desirable … way different. So we'd be in the hospital for as long as they would allow us to be there. It was always a perpetual party. Part of those parties was always to unveil a knee or an ankle or a foot that was the size of a basketball and everybody would scream. He loved the attention, too. We all knew that he endured an awful lot of pain. That was the most difficult price, and it was constant, and nobody could help him with that. He just had to live with it. We were all very grateful that we weren't Ralph but we admired him.*

Ralph was well aware of this cycle. He knew that overexertion and an active lifestyle would eventually cause him misery. But in his mind, the suffering that would surely come was well worth the price if he could experience an ounce of normalcy. Ralph reflected on his desires:

Sunday, January 31, 1943

Only I and God can know how I prize health. It may always be outside my reach entirely, but having it now and then is enough to assure me of its blessings, although I know that what happens to me is for the best. Tomorrow I intend getting up fairly early, and want to go to Mutual [teenage organization sponsored by the Latter Day Saints (LDS) Church] tomorrow night if I am able. Oh! if my health only holds up—how rich life will be; though perhaps my destiny is charted otherwise. However things turn out, I will make the best of them, and realize that it must and surely will be for my benefit ... And, too, I can bring on sickness or become indisposed through foolish actions and over-exertion.

Ralph had much to say about his suffering in the journals he kept during his teenage years. But he also had a strong interest in world events, especially during this time of war, often noting headlines from the newspaper. He wrote about his family: his parents, Rudolph and Phoebe; older teen sisters Lucie and Alta; sister Donna, three years younger; and toddler brother Douglas. And he wrote about his friends and the activities in which he longed to participate.

Tuesday, February 16, 1943

It has been a short and uneventful day; in fact, uneventful to the point of being really dull. I did not get up until almost eleven o'clock this morning, as I was so late getting to bed last night. Although I did wake up about eight-thirty, I kept dozing off until I had to force myself to get up. Then I found that my right ankle was stiff—and is still so stiff that I will be unable to go to Mutual tonight or take part in the play. I hate to call and say I can't come; it sounds too much like a hastily thought-up excuse. However, the truth is that I could not begin to go; that is, not without a wheelchair. I don't think my ankle will stay bad long; it will probably go away tonight, although it might stay on and get worse. I only hope . . . that I will be in good enough health tomorrow and after to take part in social affairs, and that I will have sense enough to refrain from doing more than what I am capable of.

Tuesday, March 2, 1943

It has turned out to be a pretty punk day, although I feel good mentally, because of accomplishing a decent amount of schoolwork. My ankle was better this morning, but about one o'clock this afternoon, my left arm started getting stiff, and by four o'clock I had to take a pain capsule to combat the pain. It is still terribly sore. It is the first major attack I have had in a long time—three months. This afternoon I was left alone with Douglas; and with him, my sore arm, and an overpowering sleepiness caused by the capsule, I about went nuts. Nobody in the family feels very good tonight. At this moment, I am sitting on the davenport, Mother is beside me, so is Alta, and Lucie is sitting on the piano bench putting up her hair. Douglas is in bed, and Donna is tending babies. I only hope that my arm does not stay bad for long (I tell you, it is really sore!), and that I will be able to get around good again before long. Close now at nine-fifty . . . G'night. (Will probably sleep on the davenport tonight; don't know if I'll rest well.)

Wednesday, March 3, 1943

I really didn't think I'd feel good enough to write this entry tonight, as I have really suffered last night and today from a fierce left arm. And my right knee is swollen and right ankle almost unusable, as well. (Dr. West, who came over this afternoon to give me a shot in this arm, thinks that it is the result of some blood deficiency, which cannot be observed in laboratory tests, and which can be remedied only by occasional transfusions.)

Last night, as I was unable to sleep except for dozing off and on, I listened to [music on] the radio until after two o'clock am, sitting in the armchair; and then read, dozed, and just endured. It was anything but pleasant. The same for today. One good thing, however, is that I have a good appetite. Man, I've really eaten a lot! Read from Reader's Digest, *too, and now, having taken a pill to combat pain, feel really dopey and drowsy. This account is being sketched roughly in pencil, but will be retyped [Ralph typed all his journal entries] when and if I feel able. I am sitting on the davenport at the moment, and my arm feels fairly good, but hurts very much nonetheless.*

Do not know how I will rest tonight. Time will tell. But I do hope that I do get well soon, and am not subject to a series of attacks like the one I am enduring at the present. G'night.

Today's happenings: U.S. Air Force in South Seas sinks ten Jap warships, twelve transports, and destroys fifty-five planes … Berlin suffers from gigantic air-raid … Russian middle-sector offensive rolls on.

Friday, March 5, 1943

Since Wednesday's entry, I have not improved at all, and am at present worrying my head off about all sorts of impending disasters. It does me no good to worry, I know, but I cannot help it (although I am trying).

Wednesday night was pretty bad. I slept only in restless snatches, as my arm got steadily worse. Finally, toward morning, I was able to lie down, and with the help of pain capsules, slept until almost noon. Then I went into the bedroom and slept some more. Read from Reader's Digest that night before going to sleep.

Slept pretty good last night, although I cannot get along without pills to remedy the pain. This morning, I have read Reader's Digest, and am very nervous and restless … There is a chance that I may go to the hospital for a transfusion, but I do not know for sure. Unless I get well pretty soon, without a relapse, I think I am pretty certain to have a transfusion … Close now, and may not make another entry for quite a while, depending on how I feel. S'long. (Am going to bed right now to rest. Feel very tired.)

Sunday, March 7, 1943

My arm at the time of this entry is still as bad as ever, but I feel fairly good otherwise. I am writing this report while lying in bed, and doubt if it will turn out to be at all legible … I am going to stay in bed all day today.

Friday was a bad night, as I slept only after four in the morning, and the pain was really fierce. I think the reason for the severe pain was my sitting up most of the day, and the consequent flowing of blood into my arm and increasing its swelling. I slept until twelve noon Saturday, read the Reader's Digest *and listened to the radio most of the time. My appetite kind of dwindled, too. My arm was as sore as ever. No one in the family felt very good, especially Douglas, who had a very bad cold.*

Saturday night, which was last night, I slept very little again until early in the morning, my arm hurting severely, Douglas waking up, crying at intervals, etc. Anyway, I did have a good sleep after taking several painkilling capsules, and going out on the davenport to get feeling good. My knee is kind of swollen, my throat and jaws are very sore, and I do not have any idea as to how things will turn out.

The war news is fierce; many decisive things happening—too many to write about. S'long.

Today's news: Germans begin a withdrawal from Tunisia, Africa; U.S. General George Patton arrives in Djebel Kouif, Tunisia.

Tuesday, March 9, 1943

I am, at the moment of this writing, in bed in room 205 of the LDS Hospital. It seems so funny to be in here, when just a week ago I was going strong. But I am just here for a transfusion. If possible, I want to go home in the morning.

Sunday night I slept well; Monday my tongue was quite swollen, which brought about the decision that I should go to the hospital for a transfusion. Last night, too, was a bad night, as I was not sleepy until late because of a long mid-afternoon nap, and my arm was very painful. (Just stopped to talk to a nurse for several minutes.)

This morning I rose at seven, had a bath, and then came downtown with Dad in a taxi, and checked into the hospital. Talked with Martelle, who gave me my blood transfusion). Dad stayed until about eleven, after which he went home. I had dinner then, rested most of the afternoon, and had supper, talking to a few nurses in the meantime. This evening, Mother came and I visited with her. Lucie came up later, and she visited for about two hours.

My arm's quite sore still, but I think that I am getting better. Enough, as I need my rest. S'long.

Wednesday, March 10, 1943

It has been a day to remember, not for the fact of its being outstanding, but for the fact of its incongruity—being in a hospital in the morning, and being home and feeling really good in the afternoon.

Last night I did not sleep very good, and I called for several grains of some sort of "pain-alliever," but it did not help, and I did not get to sleep until about three o'clock am. The nurse woke me up at six o'clock, after it seemed that I had just gotten to sleep, and I had breakfast, a blood test, and slept until eleven. Dr. West notified me that I could come home, and told me that my blood was almost "above normal." Had my dinner then, and after reading a bit from a Liberty *magazine, Mother and Dad came, and I got dressed and checked out of the hospital. Since I came home this afternoon, I have had a craving for milk, and have drunk three tall, cold glasses of it; I guess it is because I wanted some so badly yesterday in the hospital when there was none available.*

It has been a fair day out, quite warm, although there was a chilling north wind present; but it thawed some, melting most of the snow that fell to the depth of an inch several days ago. The sky was azure-blue, with a few light, fleecy clouds ornamenting it here and there; and a gold sun proved inviting. All in all, it has been quite nice out … I can hardly wait until I am well enough to be out and around again. Boy, am I going to have a good time! If I get well enough, I am going to take some girls out. And I am going to accomplish a lot of schoolwork.

I am accumulating quite an amount of diary entries. The worth of the time spent each day in reporting the day's activities is becoming apparent.

Today's happenings: Flaming Nazi Drive Sets Back Reds (Main Headline in the *Post Register*). Startling Hitler Counter Attack

Nears Kharkov. Hurled back 100 Miles With Loss of Eight Key Cities, Russian Armies Battle to Save Great Winter Prizes. Munich Burns as Bombs Fall. Home of Nazi Party Raided in Heavy R.A.F. Plane Attack. British Jab Mareth Line. Powerful Eighth Army Proves Nazi Defenses In South Tunisia. *(No reportable news from South Pacific.)*

Monday, March 22, 1943

About six o'clock this morning I was awakened by a violent ear ache, the probable result of my going downtown with a wet head when it was so cold out last Tuesday. I got up, treated it, took a couple of anicins, and went back to bed, sleeping pretty good until about nine-thirty. Then it started up again, and I have had a terrible time. It really hurts. I can scarcely hear out of it, too. And it is bleeding a bit and draining. I have accomplished no schoolwork at all, and do not know when I will get to it again. Surely not until I feel much better than I do at present ... I don't know how I'll get along tonight. I will continue to stay out on the davenport at least until Dad comes home. I only hope I can rest.

Tuesday, March 23, 1943

Last night, after finishing my diary entry, I lay down on the davenport and listened to the radio. Now and then, when I got up to change a station on the radio, my left ear would throb so violently that I dreaded it. Came back over on the davenport and hardly slept at all until about three or four in the morning. Today my ear felt better, although the pressure in it grew worse, and I have no energy. This afternoon I received two new books from my book club: Rivers of Glory *by F. Van Wyck Mason and* The Conquest of Mexico *by W.H. Prescott. They're both really good. I used up all my energy just fixing the paper covering on one. The covers are usually a bit torn about the bottom, and I repair them. But today that little chore taxed my energy more than anything has for a long time. It shows how any sort of pain weakens me.*

My ear started bothering me quite a bit this evening, but a couple more anicins and I felt much better. I went to bed then, sleeping fairly good all night (although I was awake several hours early in the morning from the pain).

Wednesday, March 24, 1943

Got up about ten o'clock this morning, and spent the day alternately in bed and lying on the davenport in the front room. My ear is draining quite a lot, but is still terribly sore, with a seemingly awful amount of pressure within it. I have needed anicins all day to put up with the pain, and have kept a hot pad against it most of the day. Have read a bit, but even reading wears me out … Douglas hasn't been feeling too good today, either, but has had a good time nonetheless.

We had chili today, and boy was it good! I ate dinner at the table, which wore me out. My ear is quite bad, and I imagine before I can rest I'll have to take something to remedy the pain … The family has said that it has been glorious weather out today and yesterday. Wish I could be out to enjoy it. And again I am getting behind in my bookkeeping, darn it … My right ear is a bit clogged up also, tonight. I hope nothing bad develops in it. And I hope my left ear gets well soon.

Thursday, March 25, 1943

I am still feeling pretty rotten, because of what Mother calls a "gathered ear." It is terribly painful, almost more so than was my arm several weeks ago. And I am absolutely lacking in any sort of pep. However, I think it is going to get better from now on, as it has been draining quite a bit this afternoon and evening, which will help it.

Last night my sleep was erratic; I slept on the davenport until early this morning, and then went into the bedroom to finish the night ... This morning I went down to Dr. West's office with Dad in a taxi about ten-thirty. The doctor gave me a shot of medicine in the arm and treated me for my ear. Came home about twelve-fifteen and lay down, being actually worn out. This afternoon I have done nothing much besides talk to the family and listen to the radio ... I feel pretty good outside of my ear, although right now my knee is a bit swollen. I think I'll be active again before long.

Dr. West keeps reiterating that he surely would like to take my tonsils out; I wouldn't doubt that some time in the not too distant future he may attempt to remove them.

Today's news: A Big Allied Offensive is On in Tunisia. In Russia The Reds are Pushing Ahead on the Central Front and Holding the Germans on the Southern Front.

Saturday, March 27, 1943

I have shown some improvement today, although my ear is still pretty painful. Last night I went to bed around eleven o'clock, and slept fairly good, although I had to take a couple of anicins in the middle of the night. I rose this morning about ten o'clock, and after mostly sitting around for an hour, I got dressed and went downtown alone in a taxi about eleven-thirty to Dr. West's office. There I had some sort of treatment for my ear, the same as I had last Thursday. My ear started bleeding tonight again, but that is almost a good sign, as it must mean that most of the pus in it has drained.

Sunday, March 28, 1943

This has been the best day I have experienced since my ear became bad last Sunday night. I got up about eleven o'clock this morning, although I was more or less conscious of things for several hours before rising. I got dressed and then lay down, but not for long. I mostly just sat and talked with the family, and looked at a catalogue ... It was a lovely day, the sun shining, and no snow visible anywhere, although a wind was blowing which kept me inside because of my ear.

My ear is really much better; even the pain is leaving. It is still draining a bit, more blood than anything else, and I can't hear a thing with it; I am a little deaf in the other ear, too, it seems.

Monday, March 29, 1943

This has been quite an ordinary day, but there will be ample things to report on, although I do not intend this entry to be large at all. I arose this morning about ten o'clock, got dressed much later, about twelve o'clock, in between which I more or less just lay in the easy-chair. I really do sprawl over things. Had dinner about twelve-thirty, after which I played the piano a bit, and just talked to Mother and Dad and played with Douglas—he surely has been a happy person these last few days. Just actually played himself out, though, this morning. And it was really a lovely morning. I was going to go out, but before I got ready, a wind started up; and although it was not cold, the wind kept me from venturing out because of my ear, which is still better, although it is bleeding a bit yet and still aches some. And my left arm that was so sore several weeks ago is still stiff and bothers me at times. When I get an attack like that it really leaves its marks for some time ... I came out in the kitchen and closed the door this afternoon as Mother was lying down on the davenport, and retyped some older entries written during my recent sore arm. Baked bread, too, which turned out nicely.

Then I went out into the living room and sat for a while, talking to the family.

Wednesday, March 31, 1943

Well, March has almost gone by; it has really been a bad month for me, in regards to health. First I suffered my sore arm and then had this bad ear develop. And the weather was not really good, although it was typical for the month. A lot of wind would pretty well describe it. Tomorrow is April Fools' Day. I don't know if I'll be the victim of a practical joke or if the day will pass unnoticed.

I have really done nothing of interest for an awfully long time. I would so like to get out and have a good time without the fear of "overdoing it." Maybe it's for the best. That's the best consolation I can find.

I did not get up this morning until eleven o'clock. When I did rise, my head felt kind of rotten, aching and bothering me; my ear is clearing up fine, although it is awfully sore at times, and my hearing is impaired a lot, for a while at least.

Thursday, April 1, 1943

I have almost entirely forgotten that today was April Fools' Day. No one's even tried to trick me. That shows you how exciting my life is on the whole. In fact, if it weren't for my getting sick so irregularly, my life would be without variation at all. My ear quite ached, too. However, it felt better as time passed. This afternoon I thought I might go downtown, but then decided against it. With my ear yet sore, and having had a stiff ankle, it seemed unwise. It proved the correct thing to do, too. My ankle tonight is awfully stiff. If I had tried to go downtown with it, I might have really ruined myself. I don't know how my ankle will turn out. I want to get and stay well so much. Never can tell, though. S'long.

Before Ralph's diagnosis of hemophilia, his doctors were mystified by his prolonged and painful bleeding episodes. While the local doctors knew that Ralph's suffering resulted from hemorrhaging into tissues, they could not determine the cause. Even when the formal diagnosis was made at the Mayo Clinic on April 30, 1943, some doctors told Ralph that he might outgrow hemophilia.

Friday, April 16, 1943

I am not feeling very good, due to the recurrence of a hemorrhage in my left elbow. Elsewhere, though, my body feels better today. It was last night in bed that my arm became quite stiff, and this morning it was fairly sore. It has gradually gotten worse, and now I doubt if I will be able to sleep until Dad gets home with some anicins. However, the attack did not come on as suddenly as the one on March 2nd, and I am sure it will not be as bad—at least I hope it won't.

Saturday, April 17, 1943

My arm is somewhat better today, and is not, fortunately, a very bad one. But I am afraid I might be on the verge of a series of attacks, which will make my trip to Rochester, Minnesota, anything but pleasant. Dad believes that we will leave for there in a week or ten days if everything goes according to plan ... However, my right ankle is a bit stiff tonight—not sore or anything—but is not very promising. There is nothing I dread more than a recurrence of [a] terrible series of attacks I experienced a year ago this spring.

Monday, April 19, 1943

I have really felt terrible today. Even though my left arm is clearing up nicely, and my right ankle feels better, I feel much worse than I did yesterday. My knee is stiffer and I can hardly walk, and I am terribly stiff and sore all over. But my main trouble seems to be something else—an overpowering, gnawing tiredness that has sapped every bit of my energy and left me with no strength.[3] *I don't know when I've felt so worn out. This morning I did not think I would be able to last the day out; I was so tired that I about killed myself off by just writing out yesterday's entry this afternoon.*

I arose this morning about ten-thirty, and after sitting around for a while and feeling terrible, I went back to bed for about half an hour. I had no appetite and could not eat a lovely dinner that was fixed for me. For most of the afternoon, I just lay down on the davenport and rested. Finally, about four o'clock, I got the ambition to get dressed and washed up a bit. Then I sat down and by slow steps wrote out yesterday's entry from notes compiled last night.

Tuesday, April 20, 1943

I have, fortunately, felt better today—in comparison with yesterday, much better … I have really rested myself. I went to bed last night at nine o'clock (although I did not go to sleep until after eleven), and stayed in bed until about one o'clock this afternoon, actually sleeping until eleven this morning. However, I am still quite stiff all over, and my knee is still stiff and bent, so that my walking is hindered. But if I am getting well, that is secondary.

Wednesday, April 21, 1943

Am feeling still better today, the result of taking it easy. I got into bed about ten forty-five last night, and slept until about that time this morning—a good twelve hours' rest. I was not nearly so stiff this morning, although

---

[3] Recurrent, untreated bleeding can cause anemia, a low iron count in the body leading to extreme fatigue.

my right knee—the darned thing!—was still so stiff and bent that my walking today could more rightly be described as "hobbling."

After I got up, I sat on the davenport and looked at a new Saturday Evening Post, *at the same time warming my stiff parts with an infrared lamp (which, I think, helps relieve muscular and joint aches).*

On April 30, 1943, Ralph was diagnosed with hemophilia at the Mayo Clinic in Rochester, Minnesota. (See Chapter 4, The Diagnosis, to read about his journey.)

Thursday, June 10, 1943

I called a cab, and went outside and sat on the cement banking in front of our place, waiting for its arrival. It did not come for fifteen minutes, and I sat, feeling the cool morning breeze blow against my face, and hearing the usual sounds associated with summer and a nice day. The shifting gears of cars starting, the far-away sounds of town, children playing loudly, and birds and animals. I lived in the present at that moment, and cherished it. I waited in the office downtown for almost an hour before the transfusion, talking with the receptionist, Ruth Ann. She is surely pleasant to talk with. Also saw and talked to Margaret, the doctor's daughter. She is more sociable now than she used to seem. Enjoyed a brief chat with her. Then the transfusion took place, lasting less than ten minutes. About 30 cc of blood was injected into my left buttock, making it very sore.[4] *Well, the immediate section of my anatomy adjoining the point of transfusion—or, more simply, my behind—is surely sore and stiff. It is not serious, but just uncomfortable. It will probably wear off gradually. Enough. Goodnight.*

---

[4] Ralph does not describe a typical blood transfusion. In a typical transfusion, donor blood is given slowly through an intravenous (IV) line directly into a vein, not injected into muscles or tissues.

Friday, June 11, 1943

I have really felt punk today, especially this evening; in one respect, the result of yesterday's transfusion. Last night I lay awake almost until five-thirty, with no more than a few winks of sleep. My hip around the spot where the needle was injected really hurt. And I could not begin to lie on it. I either had to lie on my right side, or almost over on my stomach. And in turning, I almost killed myself. But I did see the sun rise, through the bedroom window, and it was beautiful ...

Saturday, June 12, 1943

I have felt better today, but still without too much energy, and man! *once I sit down for a while, it takes ten minutes for me to limber up so that I can walk around without being stooped all over. But my hip is better, although it is still sore. I don't know whether I am going to like receiving blood in that manner. And 30 cc doesn't seem like very much. I don't see how it can help me too much. Of course I don't need the blood itself; I just need the thromboplastin in it.*

Tuesday, June 15, 1943

This has surely been a hectic day—mentally, I mean. I have been kind of fidgety all day (maybe a bit melancholy, or fed up). In doing two large lessons of history, and taking care of Douglas all day—while he's in a sorry temperament—I just about destroyed any fragment of patience I might have had. I would have liked to throw my history book out the window and, if you'll pardon me, say "to hell" with everything, then maybe go for a long walk. But even that last avenue was locked to me, because I was not in any physical condition to go walking. My knee is stiff enough that I had to stay indoors all day.

Friday, July 2, 1943

I got up very early again this morning, before six o'clock. When I put my ankle down preparing to getting dressed, it throbbed so hard when the blood rushed into it that I thought for a moment about going back to bed. Each day, my ankle feels a little worse. The bruise on it is terrible beyond description. It actually hurts me to look at it. And yet I can walk around on my foot. But the bruise is red-purple over an area of two or three square inches, and then yellow and green on both sides, and for several inches up the leg. I'm darned if I know how I acquired the darn thing. It started last Sunday, you remember. But it was a little stiff even before I went bicycle riding. I hope it starts improving soon. I don't like it to be in the condition it is.

Sunday, July 4, 1943

I went out on the porch and read for a while. Lloyd asked me over to play croquet, and I just about refused because of my ankle, but then took him up on it (perhaps not very wisely) and played several games with him on his back lawn. I came home around five o'clock, and lay down and read. The book was Free Men are Fighting, *a compilation of Associated Press reports on every aspect of the war from September, 1933 to July, 1942. It is very good.*

The rest of the evening has been spent in reading. The folks came back from the house about six o'clock, just at the time Douglas was waking up from his afternoon nap. My ankle is quite sore tonight—not exactly painful, but not comfortable in any respect. It will probably confine me in bed tomorrow. If it doesn't, I'll be surprised; and bowled over if it starts getting better, [because it] is not at all promising.

Thursday, July 8, 1943

My ankle is better today, thank heaven, although it is far from being well. And my right knee is a little swollen, but nothing serious as far as I can ascertain. If I suffer no further attacks, I believe I will soon be in good condition. But more and more, I believe I need a transfusion—and not just an infusion, although the latter is much cheaper (so much in comparison with a $40 transfusion that I can hardly consider anything else). I didn't get up again today until eleven-thirty, and this sleeping-in is helping me, I am sure. I think I will make an effort to get up earlier in the morning, though. I am getting in rather late.

On Thursday, July 8, 1943, American newspapers reported that a B-24 sank the German U-boat 232 off the coast of Portugal. It was also the fourth day of battle at Kursk, Russia, considered the largest armored military engagement of all time. The headlines: *German General Walter Model uses last tank reserve; U.S. invasion fleet passes Bizerta, Tunisia; B-24 Liberators flying from Midway bomb Japanese on Wake Island.*

Missing from Ralph's journals are entries from mid-July 1943 to May 1944, the turning point of the war. It's likely that these entries were lost, since Ralph was determined to keep a journal about his life and world events, and was a conscientious writer. I can imagine the curious and intelligent Ralph, often bedridden from debilitating bleeds, riveted to his radio listening to the news.

The Allies were fighting the Axis coalition, the deadly war machine led by Nazi Germany. In 1943, the tide finally turned against the Axis, and their defeats mounted. The Red Army in Russia crushed the German Sixth Army in Stalingrad in the bloodiest battle ever recorded. The Allies sank U-boats in the Atlantic and drove the Nazis out of North Africa. In the Pacific arena, the Allies took the offensive and there was heavy fighting by November, including annihilation of the Japanese on the island of Tarawa. Half of all the casualties in the Pacific War occurred in 1944, the last year, as the Imperial Japanese Armed Forces were driven to succeed even if it meant *kamikaze*—suicide.

In America, Ralph would certainly have heard about massive shipbuilding programs designed to outstrip the Germans. He would know about gathering rubber and metal for wartime use, and would be affected by gas rationing. Times were tough, but the country was united against a common enemy. President Franklin D. Roosevelt froze prices, salaries, and wages to prevent inflation, which hovered around 17%. But the war created jobs, and unemployment was only 1.9%. The Pentagon, the largest office building in the world, was completed. Congressional hearings revealed—and questioned—the U.S. State Department's inaction in the face of mounting reports of mass extermination of Jews in Europe.

Ralph must have listened in awe to radio broadcasts of political commentaries, and speeches by some of the greatest leaders ever known. He may have heard the infamous speech to the Italian people by UK Prime Minister Winston Churchill and U.S. President Franklin D. Roosevelt on July 16, 1943. Both leaders beseeched Italians not to die in vain for Hitler, but to "live for civilization." Only days later, Italy fell to the Allies. To Ralph, learning about Allied victories must have been inspirational as he struggled with hemophilia throughout World War II, and to the end of his life.

Monday, May 1, 1944

Well, my nights are gradually getting better, but last night was still far from restful, though bearable. I believe it is the lack of sleep as much as anything that has worn me out. I sweated a lot last night, finally getting my pajamas so soaked that I took them off, spending the rest of the night in nature's own attire. Because of it, however, I believe I caught a cold. I'm not sure when I awoke this morning, but it was around seven, I think. I lay in bed in Mother's bedroom until the family got up. Then I got cleaned up and into some fresh pajamas in which to go to the hospital. For I was having a transfusion today.

I left for the hospital about eight-thirty, and went in the ambulance with [Mr. Wood and] Mr. Toone, who was surely surprised when he found out who was going to the hospital. I didn't have a private room this time. Instead, I was placed in Ward B on the first floor. There was only one other person in it besides myself, a young Texan named Jack, who was recovering from an appendectomy. I visited a bit with him off and on all day.

Well, they had a lot of trouble this morning getting a donor. The two we had lined up turned out to be type A. I'm type O. Earl J. was tested to see if he was my type, and the poor guy was so scared about it all he about passed out. I talked to him for a while, but he didn't match either. Finally, Peggy, who works at the hospital, gave a pint of her best red blood. It was kind of funny to have the blood of a person you've known so well and gone with in your veins, but it is a pleasant feeling. It was so darn nice of Peggy that I didn't know how to thank her. It's quite a thing, after all, to give the very essence of your body, its blood.

The transfusion went off nicely, and Mother sat and talked to me for a while. She went home about noon, and I had some dinner, though my appetite wasn't enormous. Peggy stopped in to see me this afternoon. But she went home after a while because she was kind of shaking. Golly, outside it was really an ugly day, and was either snowing or raining most of the time. This afternoon, I lay and wrote a long, humorous poem to Peggy, in regards to the transfusion. I called it "Sonnet to an 'O' Type" and it was well received by everyone who read it. But I was getting tired. The excitement of the morning was making me nervous, and I experienced a slight reaction to the transfusion. But I did get a bit of sleep and felt pretty good, though I continually turned and tossed.

Tuesday, May 2, 1944

Peggy wasn't to work this morning, and that made me feel kind of bad, because she didn't feel good on account of giving me some blood yesterday. I felt that it was my fault. Well, it was surely good to be home. I lay down on the davenport, where I talked to Mother and took it easy for a while. Peggy called up to say that she had received the chocolates I sent her and the poem. They really tickled her. Well, I tried to rest on the davenport, and did get about an hour's sleep. But I was nervous, restless, and in a terribly blue mood. I wanted to have a good cry. Nothing else would make me feel better. The ordeal of the past week had kind of worn me out mentally. I went in Mother's bedroom and lay down, and felt better soon. In there I could at least rest.

I had a terribly sore throat this evening and Mother treated it, straightened the bed, gave me a hot water bottle and some anicins, and I felt swell. A little later this evening, Douglas came in bed with me and we talked and had a lot of fun and he went to sleep at my side. Gosh, I just cherish my little brother.

Anita and Ardean showed up, bringing a real surprise. The dramatics class had purchased a lovely present for me, The Victor Book of the Symphony *[Charles O. O'Connell], and Anita presented it to me. I was so pleased and surprised I didn't know what to say. I visited with those two for a while, but must have looked such a mess that they wondered what happened to me.*

Thursday, May 4, 1944

Each night my sleep improves, with the exception of some restless moments early last night. My knee was still swollen this morning, though, and still caused me pain. I worried more about that swelling than anything. I wanted it to go down. This morning I undertook getting in the bathtub, and succeeded in having a lovely hot bath that really refreshed me. I shaved and got all cleaned up, putting on some clean pajamas. It made me feel ever so much better. I came out in the front room then, and sat on the chair. Read some, then went back in Mother's bedroom, as I still tired quickly. The devil of today, though, was that even yet my knee hurt, my hip bothered me, and the confinement of the last two weeks had made me so terribly moody and temperamental that I didn't know what to do. In the bedroom, I read and read. I soaked in all the articles from one Saturday Evening Post *and went on to another. I also had a bite to eat.*

I came out in the front room again, and found that Ardean was here. I visited with him and he played the piano—and I also had some good chili for supper. But I didn't feel too good this afternoon. Finally, about seven o'clock I went back in the bedroom, where I lay and listened to the radio until eleven-fifteen. At that time, Sandy had come home from the first night of the Senior Play, and said that it had gone over wonderfully ... Gosh, I haven't seen Anita since—golly, it was only yesterday. I surely miss her, but what can I do?

Sunday, May 7, 1944

I slept quite sound last night, and my usual "hour of pain" was but an hour of restlessness. And I was awake this morning about nine-thirty. Immediately upon awakening, I picked up the book The Robe *[Lloyd C. Douglas] and continued reading for about two hours, having my breakfast in bed. When I finally got up, laying the book aside against my will, I went in the bathroom, where I had another bath and got all cleaned up. I even got dressed in some light brown trousers. Then I came out in the front room, where I sat in the front chair, and with my typewriter on the card table before me, retyped both that poem I wrote to my dramatics class and that poem about the war I wrote last Sunday. But I lay down then. I was worrying about my kidneys, besides my knee.*

I had fears that they might be hemorrhaging. Too, my other knee had gotten a bit swollen. I was disgusted.

Monday, May 8, 1944

I slept fine last night, and awoke up this morning about eight o'clock. A surprising thing happened then: I experienced a short-lived but very terrific pain in my right side. I feared for my kidneys, but when it ended figured everything to be all right; and so I lay in bed quite happy, feeling swell, finishing the book The Robe, *and having a couple of bowls of cereal for breakfast. But around eleven o'clock I experienced a great shock. My kidneys were hemorrhaging a bit.*[5] *My heart sunk like a lead weight. It is hard to explain the terrible drop in morale such a thing brings on. But it wasn't giving me any pain, and I figured that if I was careful, I might be able to remedy the trouble at home. So I put an ice bag on my stomach, and just lay still most of the day. I read for a while from the book* 20,000 Years in Sing Sing *[Warden Lewis E. Lawes], but found myself quite tired. So I went to sleep, and didn't wake up until five this afternoon. I was better, too, I found, and that rested me mentally. My knee still bothers me a lot too, so I have a lot to worry about. This evening I have read a lot, and have had a good supper. Ardean called up this evening to say something about my being one of the outstanding students in high school this year, but I don't know much about it ... I tell you what would please me more than anything, and that's to be well.*

Tuesday, May 9, 1944

I slept quite well last night, considering my night-long efforts to keep an ice bag on my stomach, and I awoke about nine o'clock this morning, feeling good. My trouble was cleaning up nicely. By the way, I don't think

---

[5] Symptoms of a kidney bleed can include back pain and/or blood in the urine. Blood in the urine is called *hematuria*.

I've mentioned about all the trouble my right hip has been giving me. At times it is almost worse than my knee. But they're both getting better now. The swelling in my knee is way down—and well it should be. It's caused me enough trouble. I'm so darned impatient to be up and around that I don't know what to do. Graduation is next Tuesday, and I know I won't be well enough to attend. Even after my knee's better, it will take me quite a while to regain the strength in my legs. This morning I just lay in bed and thought. There wasn't anything else to do. I had a bite to eat, too, and wrote a short, sweet note to Anita. I then began reading 20,000 Years in Sing Sing. *In fact, most of the afternoon was spent with it, and also with the* Home Book of Music Appreciation *[Helen L Kaufmann]. I took out time (I had plenty of it) to read through my play* You've Got to Help Me George. *The day was rather trite and dull all in all, and left me quite discontent; besides I've had quite a backache. I don't know what caused it. This evening I've had a nice dinner, and have read the paper and written this entry. I guess I'll listen to the radio this evening. There's nothing else to do. If I don't get well soon I'll go nuts.*

Wednesday, May 10, 1944

I slept swell last night, the first night I can truly say I have rested for over two weeks. And I didn't awake this morning until about ten o'clock. I prided myself upon the fact that my kidneys were better and I felt fine. And so for a while this morning, I just lay and thought. Suddenly, I got a bit of a nosebleed, and it quieted me down. Mother went over to a store, and brought me home some ice cream and cupcakes. I lay and read from a Saturday Evening Post, *and later from a book of jokes. But I had a recurrence of my kidney trouble this afternoon, and it got steadily worse. Fortunately, my knee didn't cause me a bit of trouble, and I wasn't in any pain, so I could rest. But mentally I was quite upset. And this evening, as we had some more rain and lightning outside, I just lay and pondered. I wanted to get well for graduation, and I wanted to see Anita, and any number of things. I forgot to say that mother left again with Douglas this afternoon for a while, because Douglas was so noisy and she wanted me to rest. This evening was spent listening to the radio and worrying.*

Thursday, May 11, 1944

When I awoke this morning, my kidneys were worse, and so the decision was made that I should go to the hospital again for another transfusion. I felt terrible about it. I told my sisters not to tell anyone I was in the hospital, and I [regretted] those words this evening when nobody came up to visit me. I really felt good this morning, though. My knee didn't bother me at all, and I was in no actual physical pain. Mr. Wood and Mr. Toone came for me again, and I talked to them on the way to the hospital. I got there about nine-thirty, and was placed in the same ward where I was a week ago, but in a different and better bed. I had a transfusion almost immediately after getting there. Joe, the fellow who sold shoes at the Frock and Bonnet with Don and [me] around Christmas time, gave me his blood. I didn't get to see him.

I talked to Dad for a while, then he left. In the ward with me were two other fellows, one who had had his appendix out and the other who had had a tonsillectomy. I visited with the former a bit all day. After dinner, I wrote yesterday's journal entry, read some from the book Great Modern Reading, *dozed once or twice, wrote a humorous news sheet for the nurses, and had fun visiting with them. My nurse, Miss Ball, quite a cute kid, was a lot of fun, and we about died laughing. Well, after I got cleaned up this evening and had my supper, I just lay, hoping someone would come to see me. Mother came up, bringing my high school annual. But none of my friends showed up, because they didn't know I was there. I was supposed to have been to a banquet honoring the outstanding school students, but I couldn't attend. I got to sleep after a late snack, and really slept swell.*

May 25, 1944, headline: B-17s deploy the GB-1 guided bomb in an attack on Cologne.

CHAPTER 3

Discouraged

The important thing is not to stop questioning.
Curiosity has its own reason for existing.

—Albert Einstein

One of many childhood memories I recall is being taught to ride a bicycle. Dad had insisted that the training wheels were coming off; he said I was ready. I was … I thought. As I wobbled onto the bicycle seat, I felt as if the universe had stopped in its rotation, anticipating what was going to happen next. Dad said, "We'll start slow, and I'll follow. Don't worry, I'll hold on—just get a sense of your balance." Dad's words were comforting, but as I gazed down at the two wheels, I became frightened and immediately stiffened. The result? Suffice it to say I became acquainted with the principle of gravity. The only positive that emerged from my first experiment was learning to steer to softer ground for my certain and frequent falls. Why do I *need* to learn to ride a bike? It's stupid. I'll just walk from now on. Anything has to be easier than this.

My little-boy pride was shattered and I walked away from my two-wheeled enemy vowing never to touch it again. I begged my dad to put my training wheels back on. Wisely, he declined, reassuring me that I could learn to ride a two-wheeled bike and that we would try again tomorrow. *In a pig's eye!* Nevertheless, morning came and once again I faced the enemy. Then an amazing thing happened. As I mounted the bike, I didn't feel so wobbly. I had better balance. I was in control. After a few attempts, I was riding! I could even turn corners and stop. What had happened? How had I improved so much in only a day? I didn't dwell on questions. I was having too much fun with my new skill.

As I look back now, I realize that there is a correlation between adversity and success. The diploma of success is never attained without graduating from the school of adversity. If I had followed through with my threat and stopped trying to ride a two-wheeler, I never would have discovered the thrill and freedom of riding. It's the same with any new skill: first comes awkwardness, then persistence causes a breakthrough, and practice develops skill. You begin with Chopsticks and graduate to Liszt's *Hungarian Rhapsody*.

Ralph experienced discouragement—lots of attempts and as many failures. Courageously, he met the fearsome force of continual joint and muscle hemorrhages as he worked through each bleed, focusing his mind forward, away from the pain.

Sunday, May 28, 1944

I had a grand bath, washed my hair, shaved, and got dressed in my blue suit. I was so happy, because at long last my knee was easy to walk on and almost well. But a somber note struck then that was to trouble in ferocity. I noticed my right knee was just a bit stiff while I was standing and shaving. I didn't worry too much about it right then. I sat and listened to the radio, and waited for dinner to get ready. And I kept wishing that there was some place to go. There wasn't, though, probably fortunately for me. We had a lovely dinner, and I really stuffed myself until I had to lie down on the davenport in order to rest it off. Ardean came over and played the piano a bit, and after he left I listened to the radio until about four-thirty. Ardean came over again [later], and together we went out in front and lay on the lawn. It was beautiful out today, and hot. Well, I lay out there and read, and talked to Lillian and Joan, who were passing by. Anita called up then, and said she might be able to come over this evening. I surely hoped she could.

I sat and listened to the radio then until around six-thirty, when I went outside again. By this time my right knee was a bit sore, and getting stiffer, but I couldn't think that it was getting bad. I was sitting on the porch reading a joke book when a car pulled up in front with Anita [and] Ardean. No kidding. I was tickled to death to see Anita, and ... she stayed and visited with me this evening. We had a grand talk that I know helped to cement our friendship. And she looked so nice in her suit. It was a lovely evening, but my knee was getting worse and I was getting worried. But I enjoyed her companionship to the last moment. She left around ten-thirty, and I got into bed directly. My knee was getting painful, and I knew I was in for something bad. Ardean came over and talked to me here in the bedroom. It was a swell discussion on music, and I enjoyed it. When he left, I tried to get to sleep. I was fairly successful.

Monday, May 29, 1944

Well, I slept fairly good last night until about five am. Mother and Dad got home about that time from their vacation trip. But my knee gave me too much trouble to rest well, and I didn't get to sleep again for a couple of hours. I was terribly discouraged when I awoke this morning. My right knee was acting up just the way my left one had five weeks ago. It was painful, too. Well, I sat and lay down alternately while I wrote yesterday's journal entry. I felt so bad, too, about having to drop all social activities just as I was getting to a position where I could resume them. I wrote a letter to Anita, too, thanking her for everything, and telling her that if she wished, just to forget me as a companion until I'm well. Not that I like the idea, but that my being sick is also so unfair to her.

On Monday, May 29, 1944, in the eastern Atlantic, the 9,800-ton U.S. aircraft carrier Block Island was hit without warning by three torpedoes from the German U-549, and sank within 40 minutes. Six crewmen died.

Tuesday, May 30, 1944

Last night after taking a couple of "pain-killers" I really slept grand, and I didn't awake until after ten this morning. I spent the morning alone in the bedroom, reading and putting up with my knee. The pain was more or less bearable this morning. I also listened to Ardean playing the piano out in the front room. I seemed more or less resigned to being sick again, and so didn't feel quite as blue as I did yesterday. Early this afternoon I tried to get some sleep, but I didn't doze off; I just rested. Dad brought me back a Reader's Digest *from downtown, and I spent the remainder of the afternoon reading it. We had a terrific storm outside this afternoon, too. It really thrilled me. The thunder and lightning were so bad that at times the house almost rocked. Then it poured down until actually it was almost a cloudburst. The streets were all flooded when it ended.*

My knee started to get worse tonight, and I knew I had a terrible night ahead. I listened to the regular Tuesday night radio programs until eleven o'clock, when I turned off the radio. But even though I took pills to ease the pain, they hardly phased it. About twelve-thirty, I crawled out on the davenport, but felt worse out there. I couldn't stand it in the front room, so I went into the folks' room, where I spent the rest of the night. But I didn't get to sleep until on towards morning. The pain was so terrific at one time I broke down for a moment and cried. Finally, I was given the power to bear it, and the latter part of the night wasn't quite so bad.

Wednesday, May 31, 1944

I slept late this morning, if not well. And I could tell that my knee was easing, even if it was terrifically painful. I managed to get by all right with anicins all day, though. This morning I read a bit, and then slept, and had a hot water bottle on my feet. I slept quite a while this afternoon while Mother and Dad were downtown. It rained a bit out today, but in general the day remains quite hazy in my memory.

Thursday, June 1, 1944

My sleep last night was painful part of the time, but I did get some fairly good rest, and this morning woke up just long enough to take some anicins and go back to sleep. I finally woke up about twelve o'clock. I felt better, but my left elbow had gotten stiff and, though it didn't pain me, it was bothersome. This afternoon I lay and rested in Mother's bedroom. I almost dozed off, but mostly it was daydreams. Mrs. Watts brought me over a lovely book today, and I read it this afternoon. It is called Singing in the Rain, *and I don't believe anything has made me feel so happy to be alive. Ardean stopped in, and it was good to see him. I haven't had any company for several days, so he has been unable to see me. And he seemed so happy about talking to me this evening that it made me happy. I didn't get to sleep until late, and felt pretty good, but felt like I had an upset stomach. Anyway, it wasn't comfortable and I suffered gas pains. And that kept the ensuing night from being too pleasant.*

Saturday, June 3, 1944

I slept quite well the last part of last night, after having an anicin and a small bowl of bread and milk about one o'clock. I awoke only to have another anicin, put a hot water bottle at my feet, and go back to sleep. I awoke a second time a little after ten-thirty. Mother and Dad were going downtown. I lay in bed then, just thinking more or less, though there was little to think about. Douglas came up on the bed with me, too, and I did imitations of trains, airplanes, sheep, cows, and the like for about an hour, when the return of Mother and Dad took his interest elsewhere. I came out on the davenport then with Dad's help, and I really experienced a black mood. I was so tired of being sick and indisposed, with no end of it in sight, that I could hardly refrain from swearing like the devil. Then, to complicate things, my left arm, which has been stiff for several days, became worse and was actually sore.

I didn't do much this afternoon. I just lay on the davenport, read a speck, and talked to the family. I stayed out in the front room until about seven-thirty, spending the latter part of the afternoon laughing my head off at Sandy and Donna, who were describing a recent humorous movie picture in town. Honestly, they were all show in themselves. That was the bright spot of the day. This evening, I lay in the bedroom and mooded. Mother came in around nine-thirty, and she and I had some ice cream and cake and played a set of two-handed pinochle. I won the set, and it was a lot of fun.

Monday, June 5, 1944

I think I was awake most of last night. The light was on in the dinette, and for a while I had music on the radio. And stockings kept my feet warm. But my arm was terrifically painful, and I got so tired I almost fell over. I couldn't lie down because it seemed that to do so would bring on a pain so bad that I couldn't stand it. So I sat, and Dad came home and I talked to him, and he went to bed. I dozed for a minute sitting up, but the pain didn't ease. Mother got up later in the night, and I talked to her. Douglas, too, was a bit sick. He was running a fever, and Mother was rather worried about him. I don't recall too much of what followed. But finally morning came, and I was in such a state of exhaustion that, pain or no pain, I lay down on the davenport and went to sleep. I slept long, and then went in Mother's bedroom where I slept some more. Though I awoke off and on during the day, and had a small bite to eat once, my sleep didn't really come to an end until about six o'clock this evening. My arm had stopped hurting and was almost miraculously getting well. But the evening wasn't especially interesting, so the day passed swiftly and uneventfully along. Ardean came over and visited with me for a moment this evening just before I turned over to go to sleep. But sleep didn't come soon, though I did enjoy it eventually.

Tuesday, June 6, 1944: D-Day. The Allied invasion of Europe, on the beaches of Normandy, France, is the largest amphibious force ever assembled, with over 5,300 ships and 11,000 aircraft. When the beachhead is secure, more than 2,000 Allied soldiers will have lost their lives.

Ralph outside the Mayo Clinic, Rochester, Minnesota, April 1943

CHAPTER 4

The Diagnosis

Live your questions now, and perhaps even without knowing it, you will live along some distant day into your answers.

—Rainer Maria Rilke, *Letters to a Young Poet*

Although Ralph never wrote about his parents' emotional reaction to his mysterious, undiagnosed disorder, Rudolph and Phoebe were clearly suffering. What parent wouldn't suffer? Yet during times of vigor and health, Ralph took full advantage, and his parents allowed him the freedom to do as he pleased—to be a kid and to experience his teenage years as much as possible. Nevertheless, everyone knew it was a matter of time before he would become sick again. The nagging question was always, *What's wrong with Ralph?* But no one, not even the local doctors, had an answer.

Seeking a diagnosis, Ralph and his parents began planning a trip to the Mayo Clinic in Rochester, Minnesota. Train travel, still the common mode of transportation in the 1940s, was a boon to the Rytting family. Rudolph was employed with the railroad and, as a perk, he could travel the rails at a discounted rate. So in April 1943 Ralph and his parents traveled to the Mayo Clinic—a trip of almost 1,000 miles, requiring three days' train travel. In the evenings, Ralph wrote his journal entries by hand, and then typed them in the hotel room as he brought his beloved typewriter with him everywhere.

The Ryttings' visit to the Mayo Clinic proved pivotal, forever changing Ralph's thought process about his condition. On Friday, April 30, 1943, he and his parents finally received the diagnosis of hemophilia. In his journal, Ralph gave a full account of his trip and his feelings as the diagnosis unfolded.

Wednesday, April 28, 1943

This has been a wonderful day! Not only did I get to the famous Mayo Clinic, but I also [toured] it for the first time, and thoroughly enjoyed myself.

Last night I really did sleep grand for being on a train. I only woke up once, and that was just before midnight, and so I rested until six o'clock this morning without interruption. And the train was a wild one—at every stop there would be a terrific jerk (so I was told), and the cars would swing constantly back and forth ... The porter awakened us on forty-five minutes' notice, and we got dressed just before reaching Mankato, Minnesota, our changing point. And is Minnesota a beautiful state! Dark black earth, beautiful farms and farmhouses, lovely lakes, beautiful, neat cities—it is really a grand state! Mankato was a nice, and a fairly large city, too. I would compare it with Pocatello, Idaho, in size, though it may have been smaller. From Mankato to Rochester we rode in a chair car, but it was a nice one, and the distance was passed with amazing rapidity. All along the way, Dad, Mother, and I kept exclaiming about the beautiful farms—we couldn't get over them. Mother says she will always remember Minnesota because of them. I will, too.

About nine-thirty we pulled into the station at Rochester, and got a cab to take us to the clinic building. There I got registered and received an appointment for one-fifteen this afternoon. Then we went over to our hotel—the Campbell (where I am while writing this entry)—and got settled. We were very hungry by then, so we went over to a cafe a block east of the hotel and had something to eat. Then I had a bath and got cleaned up for the appointment …

You know, ever since I got off the train, the ground has been moving under me. Even when I look out the window, things seem to move by. That is because of my riding the train for so long. I imagine it will pass tonight. Right now, however, I still get feeling funny when I stand …

When we got back to the clinic, I had a real examination, and had my case history batted out, as well as two doctors come in on my case. Also, I got appointments for tomorrow (a blood test in the morning; ear and nose at two-thirty), and had several X-rays taken of my chest and right knee. Finally I got out of there about four-ten or twenty, and went to the lovely library here and looked at books and magazines. Then Mother and Dad came, and we went to a place called the Green Parrot, where we had a good but expensive dinner. I came back to the hotel then, and Mother and Dad went out looking for a show to see. I decided to stay at the hotel the rest of the night, as I had done quite a lot today. The two found them a show, came here for a moment, and then left to see it.

In the meantime, I have typed last night's entry, done this one, eaten some cookies, and am going to send off a couple of picture-cards to the girls at home … Outside of my window I can see the beautiful clinic building silhouetted against the late evening sky; it is almost dark. Lights are on in the building. There are quite a few cars visible on the street below, but the scene is comparatively quiet. I do think that Rochester is a grand place, though. So clean, fresh, and green that it makes some other places look pretty poor in comparison. I also met a lot of patients on my round of the clinic today; I do not know any of them today, but just talked to several … After sending off the cards I am going to write, I believe I will go down in the lobby and sit. S'long.

Thursday, April 29, 1943

Has been a blustery, windy day here in Rochester today. In fact, the wind was so strong that as we were going around the corner of the Mayo Clinic about eleven this morning, a man was blown off his feet. When we awakened, the streets were wet from rain, but during the day it did not rain at all. All three of us, Mother, Dad, and myself, slept very good last night. We really appreciated the absence of rocking and rolling that has accompanied our sleep during the last two nights. We woke on call from the desk at seven o'clock, and got dressed for an eight o'clock appointment at the Clinic. I was supposed to go without breakfast for a blood test, so that routine was eliminated. The blood testing took about two hours (mostly waiting), and then we went and had something to eat at the Barbes Cafe, a block east of our hotel. Then Mother and Dad and I came back to the hotel, and all but myself lay down and had a rest (Mother in fact slept for several hours), while I came down in the lobby and visited. (Which reminds me: Last night after writing my entry, I came down to the lobby as I predicted I would, and visited and talked with several people for over an hour. I really enjoyed myself—hearing about other states, and talking about events, persons, and places with these people.)

About twelve o'clock I went out and over to the attractive library here; it is about one and one-half blocks from our hotel. I stayed there for about an hour and a half, reading magazines and perusing books. Then went to the clinic for my afternoon appointment, waiting in the main lobby for about half an hour until Mother and Dad showed up. It took about two hours to get through with an ear, eye, and throat examination (again most of the time was spent in waiting), and then we went and had dinner at the [Barbes] Cafe. From there, Mother and Dad came back to the hotel while I went to a show at the Chateau Theater. It was It Ain't Hay, *with Bud Abbot and Lou Costello. It was funny and nonsensical. I enjoyed it. (Also, I found a roll of film in a shop, and we can probably get some pictures while we are here.) After the show, at about nine o'clock tonight, I stopped in at a drug store for a drink of ginger ale, then came to the hotel, and have typed ever since. Right now I am sitting in a little room off the main lobby, typing. Between the first and second paragraphs of this entry, I stopped and talked for almost forty-five minutes with a man from New York. I enjoyed the talk immensely, perhaps because he speaks German, and I can really interest myself in that subject. I found out about his state and told him about mine. He went to his room just a moment ago.*

It is awfully late now. I have written a card to the girls back home and was going to write a letter, but will have to postpone that until morning now, I'm afraid. I sign off at 11:06 pm.

Friday, April 30, 1943

Today has really been a momentous day—one whose decisions and verdicts will influence the whole future course of my life. I came to the Mayo Clinic for an analysis of my case, and this morning I received it.

Last night I again slept good in the Campbell Hotel. It may not be the swankiest or most luxurious in Rochester, but it is certainly a nice, clean, comfortable hotel. I was awakened by a desk call at seven-thirty this morning, got dressed, and as I was the only one who was hungry, had breakfast by myself at the Barbes Cafe. It was a better day out than yesterday, although still windy and a bit cold (the wind is much worse than any in Idaho). After that I went to the clinic at nine o'clock with Dad and Mother. After waiting quite a while for our "desk call," we were ushered into a doctor's office, and were there met by two doctors, one of whom examined me Wednesday.

Their diagnosis was straightforward and outright. It is fairly clear that, regardless of any absence of hemophilia in Mother's family for several generations back, I am a hemophiliac. There is not really anything that can be done for this condition, either to remedy it or cure it. So I will probably be subjected to attacks in my joints, all of which can be affected, all of my life, unless a certain remedy, which scientists have been working on for years, is found, or I outgrow it—very, very unlikely.[6] *However, the attacks will perhaps come in cycles, and for long periods I may be without them completely. The only thing that can be done to help them or ease them is, before a hemorrhage has developed badly, to have a transfusion or to take them at certain intervals. I will be able to be active between the attacks, although I will have to avoid all accidents whatsoever, because bleeding with me can be very serious. And I will have to avoid strenuous exertion or physical exercise. However, I might be able to dance a bit in moderation, ride my bicycle, and walk a fair amount. All in all, I will be able to live a fairly normal life, notwithstanding the attacks, during which I will have to just rest and take it easy until they pass. However, it is possible that I still may outgrow this disease, even if the possibility is remote, and there are many chances that soon a needed component of the blood, which I lack, may soon be found in stable quantities …*

The diagnosis report and instructions took about two hours, so we did not get out of the clinic building before twelve-thirty, including our checking out. By the way, the charge for my case was only $64, which is very reasonable.

I cannot here attempt to describe my feelings when I heard the diagnosis. To hear a physician say that you are to have this pain and indisposition all of your life, even though at times it may not bother you, is like hearing a sentence pronounced upon you. He gave me very little hope for recovery, although I will always have hope of that, no matter what anyone says. I really surprised myself how calmly I took

---

[6] It is impossible to outgrow hemophilia.

it, though. I don't know for sure how Mother and Dad felt, although I know they felt bad to think that nothing concrete could be done to help me. But for one thing, just getting a definite analysis is worth the whole trip. Now there will be no doubt in my mind as to what to do in case of sickness or emergency. My mind is cleared of any misunderstanding and doubt. That will be an asset to my parents, too. You see, last November when I was in the hospital, the doctors were in favor of having my spleen removed. But Mother and Dad, in the face of this united opinion, decided against it. And it turns out now that an operation of that sort might easily have proved fatal for me. No chances like that lie ahead, now that the question is settled ... And medical science is not yet infallible. It might even turn out that I do not have the disease the doctors said I had, though I doubt that such will be the case. I think the diagnosis was fair, just, and as correct as could be expected in face of all the evidence presented. But even now at times, if I think too much about what was told to me, I get kind of shaky and nervous; but that is quick in passing, and comes infrequently.

Thursday, June 3, 1943

Mother and Dad came home, and brought a new cane for me. It is to help me get around better when my legs are bothering me. It is a nifty, light wood cane. I'm sure that it and I will soon be real friends.

Thursday, July 1, 1943

I got up at five forty-five this morning; my ankle didn't feel good at all. It is gradually getting sorer, it seems. But nonetheless I had a full, satisfying, entertaining day, and really accomplished a lot. I got to work on my history directly, and close to five hours later, had two whole lessons to my credit. And all of this in the morning; it shows the worth of rising early. The only real strain that involves is during the moment of climbing out of bed. That combines the tortures of a hundred Purgatories.

A hundred Purgatories … unrelenting, throbbing, burning, agonizing pain for hours, sometimes for days. That's what a joint bleed feels like, and Ralph knew the feeling well. But he had actually received good news at the Mayo Clinic: He now knew he had hemophilia, and he knew how to treat it.

Hemophilia is a blood disorder. One of the blood proteins, or "factors," that normally work together to form a clot is missing or inactive. For about 80% of people with hemophilia, this missing protein is factor VIII. Factor VIII deficiency is also called hemophilia A, or classical hemophilia, and was the disorder of the Russian Tsarevich Alexis. Factor IX deficiency, which affects about 15% of people with hemophilia, is also known as hemophilia B, or "Christmas disease," named after the person first identified with it in 1952. While Ralph had hemophilia B, no one understood this distinction at the time of his diagnosis. He was simply told that he had hemophilia.

The lack of even one of these proteins means that the blood can't form a stable clot to seal a leaking blood vessel. External bleeds can be treated with pressure and bandages. But this won't work internally, in the abdomen or brain, or inside a joint. When a person with hemophilia injures an ankle, knee, or elbow—all prime areas of movement and activity—blood seeps slowly into the joint. Within hours, the joint swells, feeling hot and painful. Without treatment, the blood will eventually pool in the joint and clamp off the bleeding vessel. But by then, much damage has been done. Pooled blood can take hours, even days, to reabsorb into the body; and it corrodes the smooth, glistening cartilage that covers the bone ends and allows pain-free movement. Over time, people with hemophilia can develop arthritis from untreated bleeds and can even be crippled.

When Ralph was a teenager, treatment required time-consuming whole blood transfusion. During the time it took to travel to the hospital, be admitted and get prepped, the bleeding continued to cause damage. Hemophilia treatment in the 1940s could easily have taken an entire day and even an overnight stay if there were complications. When researchers discovered how to diagnosis the missing blood protein and learned how to separate out factors VIII and IX from whole blood, commercial factor concentrate was created in the mid-1960s. With this groundbreaking discovery, patients with hemophilia could now simply reconstitute and inject the commercial, bottled factor. This scientific advance reduced treatment time from a day to a few minutes. Bleeding was stopped sooner, eliminating pain, protecting joints, and normalizing life.

CHAPTER 5

Legacy

The heights by great men reached and kept
Were not attained by sudden flight,
But they, while their companions slept,
Were toiling upward in the night.

—Henry Wadsworth Longfellow,
The Ladder of Saint Augustine

After Ralph's diagnosis, he rarely discusses hemophilia in his journal entries. Yet the activities and thoughts that he describes show clearly how he felt about it.

Tuesday, August 17, 1943

Well, this is a start of a new life, in a way, for me. I hope it is prolonged. I went to school today for the first time in almost three years, and I loved it. If I seem to describe what to others may just be routine, I hope you will forgive me. It is so new and thrilling to me that I just can't pass over it lightly.

Ralph Dean Rytting, age 16

From the musical *Shenandoah* come these simple yet powerful words: *If we don't try, then we don't do; and if we don't do, then why are we here?*

Within the bleeding disorder community, we should ask: Are we trying to preserve and build upon the legacies that have been left for us? We can't ignore the foundation created by early pioneers who shaped the treatment that now exists. Their suffering led to medical discoveries and faster treatment. Today we have excellent commercial blood-clotting medicine, rapid infusions, and a normal quality of life. Hemophilia patients can play sports, attend school, and travel freely. Sadly, freedom came with a price. In the 1980s, people with hemophilia and others receiving blood transfusions were infected with HIV. This tragedy galvanized the hemophilia community which helped win legislation protecting our nation's blood supply and requiring more thorough screening of all injectable drugs. The deaths of people who contracted HIV and hepatitis C led pharmaceutical manufacturers to develop factor concentrates derived from human genes, not human plasma. As good as these efforts have been … *are they enough?* I believe that "good enough" is when burning joints are completely alleviated and when the body can be re-engineered to create its own clotting factor. As numerous as our accomplishments have been for people with hemophilia, we can't stop trying to reach even loftier goals.

We must move forward, just like those courageous individuals who met and overcame bleeding disorders—and created legacies. As the hemophilia community adds to these legacies we also draw upon them. We must never forget them. The legacy of Ralph Dean Rytting is just one example of a person who suffered the full spectrum of hemophilia yet lived an extraordinary and inspiring life. There are many other examples, including family members and professional staff. Their stories are worth recalling and preserving. I view this book as only a beginning and hope to gather other inspiring stories that honor and build upon the past. These people are our mentors and our heroes. Heroes: an ideal name for those who have made it possible for patients with bleeding disorders and their families to better enjoy today.

I never knew Ralph Rytting, but he was a hero to me. I was born his grandson in 1975. In 1971, at age forty-four, Ralph died in his sleep. His heart simply stopped. If this great man hadn't kept journals, I would never have known him or received his legacy. Now, today, the past shines brightly for me and my personal challenges seem lighter. I feel new energy to face the future and conquer the impossible. This is the legacy of every hero. Each new generation receives the heritage of the past, and from it creates the present and the future.

Wednesday, May 14, 1969

I don't know how the problem of our individual survival is resolved, whether in truth it is intensity of living rather than length. Or whether we can meaningfully in and of our efforts greatly affect its duration should that be so significant. But I greatly suspect that there are those who survive incredible odds, and from the sheer "will" (both mortal and Divine) reach the calmer waters of a sheltered bay, though it might be called instead "home," "success," "old age." But perhaps never again—having known the exultation of overcoming the unknowable and the frightening, having conquered our fears—never again can the soul be so complete in this life.

Several facts to me are at hand: A young boy, born with a devastating and incurable disease in a small town in Idaho in the middle 1920s, has heard his imminent death pronounced many times by knowledgeable men; and, having known at least once in this life the separation of spirit and body, has felt the absolute duality of that spirit and body—one immortal, the other so perishable. After all of these, this same boy, now older, on this beautiful morning is recovering from his first major surgery—the removal of his gall bladder (pretty good for a hemophiliac, eh?). And he sees ahead more hope than life has ever promised.

But now that [my] hardest struggle may be over, am I perhaps not the poorer in part for the loss of those sometimes anguished, yet burnished, golden, intense years?

Still, the future reaches out to me, and its few brief glimpses tell me that if none on earth cared—and so many have and do—I have a Divine Father who cares, and His Son, who has suffered everything that humankind can endure to ensure that I could return to that Father if I so willed and ordered my life.

Ralph Dean Rytting, age 42

The Rytting family, 1944: (standing, left to right) Donna (15), Alta (18), Lucie (20); (seated, left to right) Ralph (17), father Rudolph, Douglas (3), mother Phoebe. © 1944 L.W. Bacon, Idaho Falls.

Ralph and Georgia Rytting, 1948

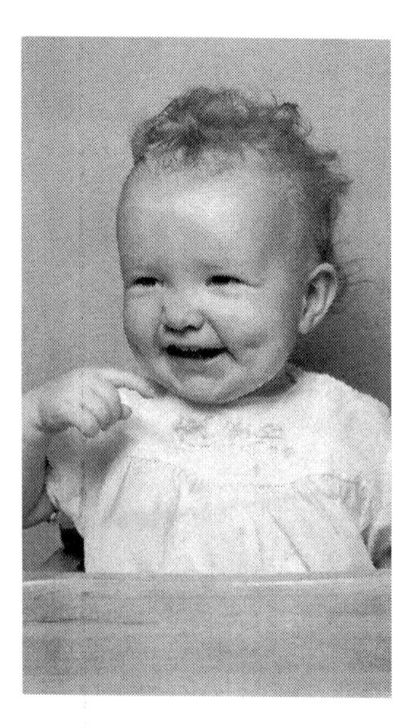

The author's mother: Ralph and Georgia's second child, daughter Elizabeth "Buffie" Rytting, 1953

Ralph and Georgia with their first child, son Colby Rytting, 1952

CHAPTER 6

Miracle at Sea

Albert Einstein said, "There are two ways to live: you can live as if nothing is a miracle; you can live as if everything is a miracle." I believe in miracles. I know that Ralph's survival of hemophilia in the mid-twentieth century, with limited treatment, was miraculous. Yet of all the injuries, procedures, and sufferings he endured, perhaps nothing was more miraculous than his incredible recovery at sea, at age 29, aboard the SS Samaria. Ralph's wife Georgia witnessed and recorded this account while the young couple was traveling home from a 1955 European concert tour with the Mormon Tabernacle Choir.

Miracle at Sea
by Georgia Rytting Shaw

My husband Ralph and I were two days out of Le Havre, France, on the SS Samaria, returning to the United States following a European tour with the Mormon Tabernacle Choir. We had been talking with some friends on the deck of the ship when Ralph began to complain that he was feeling ill and retired to our cabin. A few hours later, he became very sick to his stomach. He sat up in bed and vomited two quarts of blood into a basin. I immediately ran up two flights of stairs to the doctor's quarters for help. When the doctor hurried back with me and saw the blood in the basin, he exclaimed, "Oh, no! Oh, no!"

Ralph needed an infusion of whole blood now, but there was no supply on board ship, and there was no cross-matching equipment to test donors. Giving him the wrong type of blood would likely kill him. The doctor did the next best thing: He gave Ralph a transfusion of three pints of pooled plasma. But the hemorrhaging continued. Finally, the doctor had no choice but to risk calling for donors and giving transfusions of whole blood. We knew that Ralph had O positive blood, and we began a frantic search throughout the ship for anyone believed to have that blood type. When we had gathered a group of probable donors, the doctor began giving Ralph what was to be a long series of transfusions—fifteen in all.

I cannot express the anxiety I felt as each new batch was administered to my husband, each one suspect and potentially lethal. All I could do was offer a silent prayer over each donation, and hope that the donor was not mistaken about his or her blood type.

As news of Ralph's struggle for life spread throughout the ship, passengers of diverse backgrounds made a collective effort to petition God for help. The members of the Mormon Tabernacle Choir fasted, and some passengers fasted with us. One woman said to me, "I am not a praying person, but I want to pray for your husband now." A man said, "I am old, but I asked God to take some of my strength and give it to Ralph so he could live." Such support buoyed me. But just as the miracle of the transfusions was beginning to save Ralph's life, another adversity would threaten it.

A violent storm broke upon the ship. The sea became terribly rough, and the crew informed us that conditions would persist for another forty-eight hours. Our ship was tossed to and fro, almost helpless against the turbulence. Many people became seasick. The fierce pitching of the ship caused Ralph to lose more blood, and soon he became so ill that one of his lungs collapsed. Fearing for his life, I begged the doctor to summon a seaplane to fly him to a hospital.

"The waves are thirty feet high," the doctor said. "A plane would be dashed to pieces."

Now, one truth became obvious to us all: Unless the ocean calmed, Ralph would die. I asked the members of the choir, and many of the people who had supported us, to come together and pray for the storm to cease. I had never offered such an urgent prayer. We waited and watched. Within the hour, the storm abated. A friend came to Ralph's room in the infirmary, and motioned me to look out the porthole at the glassy, calm water. The sun had just broken through the clouds, beautiful, bright, and clear. My friend said, "Did you ever see such a beautiful sea?"

The calm provided Ralph a respite for the night, and his condition stabilized for a few hours. Then, early in the morning, his body began to fail. His heart started beating so rapidly that the doctor couldn't make an accurate count. Suddenly, Ralph's heart stopped altogether.

Within a few moments, the doctor managed to revive Ralph, but for the next thirty-six hours Ralph was to face the worst period of his battle for life. Barely conscious now, he held my hand limply and said he didn't know if he had the strength to hang on. He said he felt as though his spirit was fighting to leave his body—that if he let up for just a moment, his spirit would slip away.

During that thirty-six-hour period, Ralph's heart stopped three more times, and he had to be given adrenaline to bring him back. After each episode, the doctor tried to prepare me by saying, "Your husband doesn't have a chance of living through this. I cannot give you any hope." Throughout the entire ordeal, good people on the ship continued to petition God and to fast. They lined up to offer more of their blood. As the passengers joined in our fight for Ralph's life, I fought to drive out all doubt, repeating to myself, "I will not believe what the doctor says."

On Thursday morning, Ralph "died" and was resuscitated yet one more time. When he regained consciousness, he turned toward me, so weak that he could hardly speak. He was perspiring profusely. I sat beside him, weeping, stroking his forehead.

"What chances have I got?" he asked me. His tone was weary. He seemed to have no fight left. Before I could answer, Ralph closed his eyes and fell into a deep, peaceful sleep. I bowed my head there at his bedside and a feeling came to me as if to say, he has suffered enough.

When Ralph awoke four hours later, he had renewed energy to fight for his life, and from that moment on he began to improve. On Friday morning, a nurse came into the infirmary, opened the curtains, and let the sun stream into the room. Ralph wept like a child. He said, "I thought I would never see the sun again."

Then the nurse began to cry. She said to me, "I've never seen anything so amazing in my life. At four o'clock this morning I was sure he wouldn't make it, and now look at him! I will never again doubt that miracles are possible."

I shall always remember that Saturday morning when Ralph was wheeled from the SS Samaria to a waiting ambulance in Québec. The entire side of the ship was crowded with 1,200 friends: choir members, crew, passengers, and medical staff who had all fought for Ralph and prayed for him. They waved, applauded, and cheered us. That memory will last us a lifetime.

PART TWO

Keystones to Living

Your pain is the breaking of the shell that encloses your understanding. Even as the stone of the fruit must break, that its heart may stand in the sun, so must you know pain. And could you keep your heart in wonder at the daily miracles in your life, your pain would not seem less wondrous than your joy …
The selfsame well from which your laughter rises was oftentimes filled with your tears. And how else can it be? The deeper that sorrow carves into your being, the more joy you can contain.

—Kahlil Gibran, *The Prophet*

Ralph holding his brother, Douglas, circa 1942

BACKGROUND

Ralph Rytting respected life, and found interest and joy in the small details of nature. His battle with hemophilia affected his body, his emotions, his faith, and his spirit. Yet in spite of his disorder—or because of it—his life was filled with observation and reflection. Often, a "handicap" in one area of life seems to strengthen other areas, just as the loss of one of our five senses strengthens the other four. Ralph's frequent confinement surely contributed to his perception of the world around him and influenced his writings. Although he attended school, he was also self-educated. He was curious, thoughtful, and introspective. Perhaps suffering caused him to look inward; because of his hemophilia, he had time to reflect and read, to watch and record. His unique situation helped form his unique perspective and attitudes. He developed his own keystones to living and followed his own path to a rewarding, full life.

World War II also shaped Ralph's character, causing him to think beyond his immediate challenges. Although his physical activities were greatly limited by hemophilia, he still believed he might be drafted into the army during those turbulent years. Every day, as news arrived from the war, he recorded his thoughts on politics, security, death, and suffering. Perhaps Ralph was able to relate to human suffering because he battled his own war with hemophilia. His concern for the welfare of others is evident in his journal entries; as one who suffered, it bothered him to know that others were in pain. He wished he could provide a healing balm to ease the ills of society during that chaotic era.

CHAPTER 7

War

1943

It is getting on toward twilight outside, a chill is coming into the air, the house lights have been turned on, and we are preparing for another uneventful night. It is surely wonderful that we are so secure, so safe and unmolested, while the world is in turmoil.

Friday, February 5, 1943

Jerry C. received his call, and left this morning for the navy. They are sure taking a lot of young fellows now. It makes me feel funny, to think that I am almost at the age to join the armed forces, and take part in this brutal war. Imagine: young fellows, just my age, out there killing, getting killed, maimed, and coming in contact with horror the like of which will never be amply described. It sickens me!

Wednesday, February 24, 1943

Am going to sign off now; ...-,...-,...-,...-,V,V,V—now why am I doing that? I guess it was just the patriotism in me coming out ... Oh, this is nuts ... It's funny to think that I might be going to the army soon—sooner than I think, if I continue to get well. If I am drafted, though, I will serve in no other branch of the service, if possible, other than the medical division. Enough speculating for now.

Friday, February 26, 1943

LaMarr and I were talking tonight about the actions of some of the young kids about town. So many are so foolish—oh, ruining their lives, though they don't know it. It perhaps is good to have a war come that will bring about a reform, even though it entails much suffering. And it is too bad that innocent people have to suffer right along with the wicked. But, just the same, something needs to be done, before conditions can be remedied.

Sunday, February 28, 1943

I got out the book That Day Alone, *by Pierre van Paassen. It really goes into the rottenness, the corruption, the godlessness, and, if you like, the ruinous condition the world is in now. It analyzes the causes and probable results of current history, and the whole is not pleasant to ponder over. Honestly, when I see the pain, torture, and suffering the world is experiencing now, and then sometimes see actual evidence of it first-hand, I would like to deny God; not that I don't believe in him; I do. But just to spite him. I know that is wrong, but I can't help it. I can't honestly see why people have to suffer so. You might say they deserve it. But are they responsible for what they do? Can they choose the environment that is later going to determine their actions? No, of course they can't. And in that respect their free-agency is limited, and they are not the cause of their actions...*

I know that when people hear me talk in that respect, they sneer and say I am acting superior, am trying to prophesy and deduce (me, a mere boy) the world's problems. What do I think I am? A great man, free to deliberate such things? Or a genius with the ability to? No, I don't. But it is my duty and privilege, as much as any one else's. Leaders aren't born—they're made. Maybe even I (though I doubt it) will prove important in the making of tomorrow; it's not unlikely.

Anyway, we all are what constitute tomorrow. Unless we all assert ourselves, we aren't going to have a world that represents the whole, but just those who do the thinking—whether their thoughts are for the good or bad of the people.

Perhaps I'd better put an end to this speculating. That is one thing that might prove my downfall in certain respects. Before I can enjoy the associations of a girl, I have got to find one who can appreciate these things, and put up with my moods; as I must hers. But probably there is one with more wisdom and tolerance than I have, who will also have the shortsightedness to accept me. And there is this one thing that can be said for me: I realize my shortcomings better than most people. I know what things need improving, even if they don't improve. And I am tolerant to an extent that many others will never reach.

Tuesday, April 6, 1943

The location of the dream was indefinite—at times Shelley, at other times Idaho Falls—but I suddenly became aware of an aerial bombardment by some enemy. I saw planes and dirigibles drop bombs, witnessed the explosions, and my terror is yet hard to measure. I was actually more afraid than I think I could ever be during an actual air raid. And my fright was centered more or less around the fear that the airplanes might come back and bombard me. I alone was the target; no one else …

The dream started when I was in a house much like the one where we are now living in Idaho Falls, except that the location was Shelley. I had just come home on my bicycle late at night, when the attack came on. The bombs dropped far to the west of me, however, into what seemed to be a harbor. I remember hurrying over to another house on the north side of the street in Idaho Falls, and with some other people (there were two girls), pulling down window shades, blacking out the place completely. We were horrified. Outside, a ceiling of clouds cut out any light from the heavens, and a cool, mysterious southern breeze disturbed things. At times we would go outside and see if the airplanes were coming back …

Then I and some other people seemed to be on the move—northward, down a sidewalk—trying to escape from the terrifying and all-destroying airplanes; and after grouping around a house on a corner with many other refugees, I recall hearing about people I had known well who had been killed and maimed by the destruction; especially I remember one girl who had had her nose entirely blown off …

Then the frightful airplanes were coming again. My terror was unimaginable.

And that was my dream. It may not sound like much—one can never put down in written words the emotions felt—but it has perhaps given me a vicarious taste of what many people are suffering in the flesh at present.

Wednesday, April 21, 1943

Over the news this evening there are reports that the Nazis are on the verge of using poison gas, in which event the Allies will quickly adopt its use—and then will "all hell" literally break loose. Oh, if only we can refrain from having to resort to that godless of all godless weapons! Imagine what would happen if someone bombarded the United States with poison gas. Why, the civilians have no protection from it whatsoever! It would be devastating—ruinous. And there would surely be a mass exodus from coastal cities (where it would surely strike) to intermountain areas such as this one. Rents would go up, and conditions would become crowded in such a city as Idaho Falls. And this family is ill-prepared for such a contingency. But Dad says he is going to try and get a lease on this house for two or three years, in case we do not buy, so as to assure us living quarters if the worse comes to worse.

Saturday, May 22, 1943

I have given thought for a long time to what I am shortly to put down on paper, and have decided that it might be a good idea to record these intentions: First, it is my hope that I may take a part in the construction and rebirth of post-war Germany. This is not just an idle wish. I intend to work so as to bring about its realization. I have always admired the German people (not Nazis—don't mistake me; I hate everything that German militarism stands for), and would like to become a part of them, in order to help bring about a closer understanding between them and us. It is my intention, that after I have attained a liberal education, to go on a Church mission to Germany, and after completing that mission, to settle down, perhaps not permanently, but long enough to get a thorough knowledge and understanding of the people. May this desire be realized!

Sunday, August 8, 1943

On the way [home] I passed some drunk soldiers and sailors with their girlfriends. I was on my bicycle, and as I passed ahead of them, one yelled: "What size shoes do you wear—4-F?" If ever disgust reigned in a person it did in me. I felt like yelling, "Yes, I do, you big brave volunteers!" They were without a doubt draftees. The overgrown, drunk, immoral things were just the things that we are fighting against. Yet they wear the uniform of this country; they epitomize all the degradation that is going on in the world. I'm not ashamed that I am unable to be in military service. They need more than killers in this war. They need people who still retain an open mind toward the world situation. After all, the problems of peace are just as important, if not more so, than the problems of war.

Thursday, February 10, 1944

As we were talking [in class] about some mechanical stages, Mr. Crowley told us to be on the watch ... as we travel around, saying, "You'll all be taking trips soon around the country." To which Dale G. replied, "You ain't kidding." He meant, of course, that the army would be getting him soon, which applies to most fellows my age who are physically capable. Right now there are many more girls than fellows around school, and more young men are being taken daily to go off to the kill. It is terrible. We are going to have a lot of physical and mental wrecks before this holocaust is over.

Tuesday, June 6, 1944

I slept quite well last night, but awoke early this morning to the sound of calling voices outside. I roused myself from my slumber to hear the young, sharp voices of newsboys shouting, "Extra, Extra, the invasion is on." I listened for a moment before I comprehended what was going on. People have been waiting for years for the news of landings on the coast of France. It had come at last. And last night, I remember a beautiful full moon shining in through the window. Now it is rather haunting to think that same moon was shining down on a channel—a channel swarming with ships, thousands and thousands of ships—and on 60,000 airborne troops falling from the sky onto darkened and hostile land. Shining on airports from which thundered 11,000 airplanes, the greatest air armada of all time. You feel so small at such times.

I called to Mother and told her to turn on the radio. Sure enough, invasion news was humming over the ether. It was around six o'clock then, and for about three hours the whole family listened to news, eyewitness reports, and news analysis broadcasts. We were all excited—I even literally shook. Just awfully nervous. In fact, when we turned off the radio about nine o'clock, I had a terrific headache.

This evening, we listened to the radio, and honestly the humbleness of everybody made you feel deep the righteousness of our cause—despite the horror of the war. The regular comely programs were instead almost devotional; beautiful and inspiring singing was to be heard constantly. I don't believe people in America have ever been so deeply touched or ever seemed so sincere and thoughtful. Truly, this day, D-day, the day of invasion, is one to remember.

CHAPTER 8

Philosophy & Nature

Tuesday, January 26, 1943

I couldn't help noticing the sky tonight on my way to the depot. It was an inky, bluish black, but in the east, near the horizon, was a careless splotch of greenish silver, where, hidden by wafts of slow sifting vapor clouds, was a full moon. It was really impressive, and when I noticed it, I made at the same time a mental note to put in writing what I had seen.

Wednesday, January 27, 1943

I just pulled back the curtain from the kitchen window, and I'm going to tell what I see.Well, the ground is all covered with a light layer of white, wet snow, which no doubt will melt soon unless it snows some more this evening. The sky is veiled with a light, though thick, drape of brume, a greyish-blue color, typical of winter, which shows no variation except for a portion toward the south, where a rift shows some light, creamy-red clouds, which a late sun is striking. A car just passed, but I was too busy looking at the sky to see what kind it was.

Monday, February 1, 1943

I am expecting to go down to the doctor's office tomorrow with Dad, to get a shot in the arm. Perhaps we'll do something while we're down there. Time will tell. Which reminds me: Time is one of the funniest things I have ever come up against or thought about.

Do you know that there is not such a time as now? That's true. For life centers around two things: the future and the past. You might say that this moment is now, but is it? You can divide the moment into fractions, and the fractions into halves, and the halves into halves ad infinitum, and yet there will always be a half of something, which is always passing by, is never stationary, and is never there but always past. Yessir, it is really a funny thing … I sure do wander!

Sunday, February 7, 1943

I remember distinctly, this morning, thinking how really ephemeral all the actions and most of the thoughts we think are; how little, if at all, will be remembered of them one year from now, not speaking about one hundred years from now. And that is the trouble with the most of us. We do not live enough in the present; our thoughts are mainly centered about the past and the future. And there are also people who do live too much in the present, with scarcely a thought about the relation of the past to the present, and prepare not at all for the future. It is too bad that all the little joys and experiences that make up life cannot be indelibly recorded in our minds—for they are really what make a life good or bad.

Monday, February 8, 1943

It has been a fine winter day, and outside much of the snow which has fallen so heavily this week is melting, and in the air there seems to be a touch of spring, a subtle, impalpable air floating about that conveys a sense of regeneration and freshness.

Friday, February 12, 1943

This morning, with the clouds of vapor shrouding the earth, things had a very secluded, sinister appearance, as if some horror or catastrophe were about to strike; and the town, in sudden apprehension, crouched low and hid behind wisps of protection to shield itself.

Monday, February 15, 1943

It is remarkable how, when you marry or leave home, old ties are forgotten, new ones established, and life becomes different ... In the majority, if not all cases, we are all forgotten fifty years at the most after we die; all our experiences, and whole life, is forgotten by all (with few exceptions). It is as though life were worth nothing, that our struggles have left the world and man unchanged ... But I guess that our lives are so independent of the material world, that after death then only does our real living begin. I do not know for sure; but there has to be an answer for it all, and that is the nearest one at hand.

Monday, March 1, 1943

March has hit the Upper Snake River Valley, with the usual signs accompanying the month: A slight, but cold and penetrating north-wind is blowing; a sky full of yellow, hazy cloud banks offers strong competition to a weak sun, and, though it looks inviting out, in reality it is anything but pleasant outdoors (so the family says; I have not been out today). At this moment, the sun is hanging some thirty degrees above the horizon in the west, a golden disk, and long shadows stretch the length of the whole block. Evening is coming on; lights will be going on before long, and another day will have passed on into the timeless past, while another day arrives from out of the equally timeless future.

Monday, April 5, 1943

There was scarcely a breeze blowing, but above us the heavens were obliterated by a threatening, inter-mixing conglomeration of clouds, dark, inky-black, and the atmosphere was clear and a bit chilly, awaiting the impending deluge of rain. When we got outside, the streets were wet and reflective from heavy rain. On the way home, I took note of how fresh the air was, how clean everything smelled. Even the streetlights seemed to have been affected by the shower. Their beams seemed cleansed, brighter, and carried brightly though the night, looking like a row of livid sentinels when one gazed down a long street. And the streets mirrored everything, so that every action had its equal, and everything material its twin.

Friday, June 11, 1943

But I did see the sun rise, through the bedroom window, and it was beautiful: First of all, some purple rifts showed through the clouds in the east; these gradually became more distinct, and began to be tinted by red around the edges. Soon the rifts, parallel to the horizon, were crimson, and then the clouds dissolved, leaving a blood-red sky arching upward. It was thrilling.

Later I went out on the porch again, and was the evening ever beautiful! To the east, the skies were dark with rain clouds, but the landscape was lit up as though a solid battery of golden searchlights illumed the whole scene. Trees after the rain were an indescribably beautiful green. Houses were bright and fresh and clean in a flattering light. And birds that flew past caught the rays of the sun, bringing out their bright colors so as to stun the eye. And the whole, taken in a glance, was almost too thrilling. Green meadows and trees to the east, silhouetted against a dark mountain range, with sinister clouds overhead; closer, bright, clean, white houses; overhead, soaring, swooping, bright red-breasted robins, and vivid blue-birds; to the south blue sky, with gorgeous banks of white clouds; and overall and permeating everything, the smell of fresh earth, rain, and rejuvenation.

Saturday, July 3, 1943

I sat out on the porch this evening about an hour, from eight-thirty to nine-thirty, and watched the evening lengthen out into twilight. It is surely beautiful in this part of the country about this time. I only wish that the beauty would stay with me forever. It kind of tightens your throat to think that any lovely thing is ephemeral—to be had only for an instant, and then forever gone. The belief of life eternal, therefore, is a wonderful belief. Beautiful scenes may be lost, but newer and perhaps better ones are to be had. If, however, a person you love or think much of is forever gone, there is nothing that can refill the gap, nobody to take the place of the lost one. But with eternal life, those you love are forever yours—they are not just things of the present, but part of the infinity ahead.

Monday, July 19, 1943

My right knee has been kind of swollen today, and so I have not been too active, but have more or less stayed home and done schoolwork and written music. Last night I slept out on the back lawn in my sleeping bag. It was a marvelous night. A full moon hung in the sky to the south, and lit off the earth in an eerie silvery light. Trees cast purple shadows edged in pale yellow, and crickets gave vent to their nocturnal callings. All the animals of night were awake. The sky was obscured a bit by mist, but the brighter stars shone through. And a light, cool, south breeze rustled through the trees overhead, loosening dry leaves now and then, that would resound gently as they careened down and landed on the soft grass nearby. Sometimes during the night I would awake to the full-throated droning of airplane engines as one of those monsters of the sky roared overhead.

I seem to recall awakening three separate times to that spine-tingling sound. And then before I knew it, and much before I had slept myself out, I was awakened by the crowing of a rooster that had gotten into our backyard with his harem of six hens. I threw everything at them to try and drive them away because I wanted to go back to sleep; but they stayed on, forcing me to keep my eyes open to keep from being pecked.

Wednesday, July 28, 1943

I slept outside in my sleeping bag again last night, and it was grand. The vaulted and star-studded arch of sky above took one's breath away. I will never stop marveling at it. It is the most thrilling sight one can ever behold in a lifetime, nothing excluded. I know, the last two nights I have slept out, I would have given anything if the present could have stayed with me forever. The beauty and gentleness of it overcame me. Oh, I so hope that man had control over the time elements. I hate to think of these beauties as gone forever, even though more of the same may ever be forthcoming.

Friday, August 6, 1943

We were finishing a game when the telephone rang, and Dad notified Alta that a terrific thunderstorm was moving north from Pocatello. About fifteen minutes previously, we had noticed the extremely yellowish sky in the west and remarked about it. We went outside then … and the feeling in the atmosphere was enough to scare one to death. Everything was quiet, but from the south, the most ominous-looking clouds I have ever seen swept forward with terrific speed. The mixing, interweaving, blacking-colored vapors thrilled one—and swept all calm before them.

With the suddenness of doom, a terrific wind struck, and we hurriedly put things away from outside. Then we stood tensely awaiting the unfolding of Nature's climax. The landscape grew darker, the sky flashed to the south, and thunder echoed from nowhere with the steady rolling of kettle drums. Soon the ugly clouds were overhead, and rain started sprinkling. It never did rain hard. The lightning got brighter, and soon, to the west, jagged bolts split the sky, mating the heavens and the earth. We stood and counted until the thunder cracked and bounced in waves through the air, and knew it to be two and a half miles' distance—then one mile's distance—and then overhead. Trees moaned, and stood silhouetted green-black against a yellow sky to the west. The skies overhead flared, and the immediate vicinity lit up like day, as color came back into things for a brief instant, and the clear, deep, somber, passive green of the trees fought the night. But, as they died away with the suddenness of their birth, the fury of the gods seemed to rock the earth in that thunder that chills and thrills at once. The dwarfs up there bowling in the heavens must have made a perfect 300 tonight. The rain came faster; one tremendous bolt split the heavens and chased us indoors. It was getting a bit too fierce. But soon we were outside again, and I wondered how I would describe it. Finally we decided that a mention of the storm in the motion picture Bambi would give the best idea, for the lightning crashed and flared across the landscape like it did in that picture, and the heavens were amazingly similar. Then the lightening passed on to the north, and after an hour both it and thunder were a thing of the past. Rain continued, though, but never very hard. (This storm I hear has done a lot of damage south of here, and in Dillon, Montana, killed a circus elephant of the Cole Brothers Circus that will be in town here tomorrow.)

Friday, May 26, 1944

It is an exceptionally beautiful day today—truly a spring day in the best sense of the word. And I am sitting on the back lawn of our house, dressed only in pajamas (green) and a bathrobe (brown) and resting on a blanket. Magazines are around me, and a closed book sits nearby.

Overhead right now a bird is sounding in short fierce chirps. I look up to try and see it, but the green leaves mash his presence.

A slight breeze has been blowing all day and rustling the leaves of the trees, but a beautiful sun is also shining...The sky above is a whitish blue, covered here and there with faint nebulous clouds. A slight haze is seen as clouds form out of the blue depths. But as I lower my eyes to earth, they are met with a confusion of color that dazzles and stimulates. The prominent color is green, the green of lawns, and trees. But a reddish purple also prevails, as lilacs bloom in profusion through the block.

(That bird above me still sings.)

Our beautiful back lawn stretches out before me, and on it I visually mark the limits of the shade in which I am sitting. Where shaded, the lawn is a dark, virile green. But where the sun strikes, it becomes lighter, more delicate, and virescent.

I can also hear the quiet murmurs of voices around me in neighboring lots as we here spend another quiet day in May—a May that will be remembered, not for its beauty here, but its brutality elsewhere.

CHAPTER 9

The Arts

Ralph and I began to share a very beautiful relationship, which involved music. We wept and laughed many times through the night over beautiful sounds.

—Ardean Watts, pianist and conductor

Ardean Watts, Ralph's lifelong friend, enjoyed a distinguished thirty-year career as professor of music at the University of Utah. He was the pianist and associate conductor of the Utah Symphony for twenty-two years, and founded what became the Utah Opera Company. The following is excerpted from an interview with Ardean Watts:

I DIDN'T KNOW that symphonic music existed until Ralph moved next door ... We spent a lot of time together. I can remember setting up a speaker and records, and waking him up in the morning with Richard Strauss' *Don Juan* playing. But the classical music ingredient was a major one—it was major in his life, and spread to me, particularly. It included rituals at least twice a week where we would gather by his radio, which was a very nice one in those days. We could barely pick up Salt Lake [City]'s stations, but we could pick them up when the weather was right. There were weekly broadcasts by the New York Philharmonic, by the Boston Symphony on Saturday night, and the NBC Symphony. These were the three broadcasts every week. Otherwise, there were no classical music broadcasts on radio in that area. So we would scrunch down in front of the radio for those occasions. I can remember, for instance, hearing the world premier of the Bartók *Concerto for Orchestra* played by the Boston Symphony, and it would fade in and out to the point where we sometimes couldn't hear at all.

He had a sizeable record collection. I had a few records, very few, which I began to accumulate, but the record collection was really Ralph's. He had a relatively good sound system; I think it was a Magnavox. I remember the details very well of our using the cactus needles, and sharpening them between each play. Of course, each side lasted for four and a half to five minutes, so that if you heard Beethoven's *Symphony No. 9,* you would have to change the record nine times or more. An opera meant having twenty or thirty records. We were not particularly interested in opera, but the symphonic literature was important; and we were particularly drawn to the contemporary repertoire, which in those days was Shostakovich, Stravinsky, Bartók, Williams, Richard Strauss—and there were very few things available. My interest in the orchestral literature did not spread until Ralph moved [next door]. We used to wait for the new releases of anything that was contemporary, with baited breath, and saved our money to buy whatever we could. For instance, I remember that RCA Victor released its thousandth classical record sometime during the time we were collecting. Other people who were drawn into that orbit, some of [the girls we dated]. We'd have listening occasions at Ralph's home.

A group of us organized a quartet [See photo, Humor, page 111.] We sometimes performed nightly during holiday seasons. We were very much in demand—and we were also free, which had its advantages. Ralph was the spokesperson, and he always had thousands of jokes and kept the banter going. We'd each get a few punch lines that he would divide up among us, but he made sure he had good laugh lines.

He had extraordinary gifts as a listener. He was not an extremely good piano player. His fingers did not have that kind of steely clout. He did play well enough where he would, occasionally, do an original song. I don't know if he wrote them down or kept them in his head ... As part of our programs, we would play a little duet or something. His real gift was as a listener. Music, symphonic music especially, spoke to him in a very powerful and a direct way. That became quite interesting to us in our later relationship.

When I came back from studying in Vienna, and eventually got a masters degree, Ralph confessed to me one day that he felt very inferior because I had an opportunity to study music formally, and he wanted to know everything I knew. My argument to him then, as it would be now, is that he innately knew more music than I would ever know. He had absorbed it directly from the music, and the music theory that I knew, and he didn't know, was trivial. He was unconvinced of that. He thought of it as being a mysterious body of knowledge that held some grand secrets, and none of my protestations to the contrary could convince him at all. I never did look at him as an inferior in any way. As a musician, I saw him as an equal, if not a superior, because he knew the literature ten times better than I did then or I do now. He just listened to everything incessantly, and he retained it in a way that I could not. Very often our conversations hinged on that.

By the time I returned from my travels and settled in Salt Lake, he had established himself in his audio consulting business. He had, of course, hundreds and hundreds of friends who looked to him for advice, and it was only natural that he would be able to parley that into some type of profession. We all deferred to his judgment. It wasn't just his ear; it was also the fact that he read all the magazines, all the journals—he knew exactly what was going on. Although he wasn't a trained electrical engineer, he had ears, and that distinguished him from all of the other people who sold audio equipment ... He had his area, his realm of expertise. His collection of records was the envy of all of us. We'd always want to go [to his home] to find out how it really ought to sound. None of us ever really came close to what he offered in his own home.

To him, [music] was always a very tense experience, and laced with tears and powerful emotions, which very often, friends don't ever share. It meant so much for us to have him either lead us or join us in that kind of celebration of life. I guess I think of him in terms like that because those are values that he passed on to me.

Friday, February 5, 1943

We played some beautiful music tonight: Tod und Verklarung *by Richard Strauss, and* The Firebird *suite by Igor Stravinsky. I surely want to go through a music conservatory if possible, so that I can better understand music, and make attempts at composing, myself. I don't know if I'll ever have the opportunity, for it will take both time and money, which will be hard to find.*

Thursday, February 18, 1943

Oh—it's funny to look back on things past and usually forgotten. To realize how little we knew of things that were to come. How little we know now of things to come. But they were good times, and I'm glad that I had the opportunity to go through them. If I'd only kept a record then of things happening like I am now, how priceless it would be. Whatever I do, I must not forgo this diary of mine—no matter what happens!

Tuesday, March 16, 1943

I just sat around while the Fifth Ward Orchestra got ready to play for the Young Folk's Ward Reunion (up to fifteen years of age). Donna was there. The orchestra is pretty good, although it needs better arrangements, better musical balance, and a really good director if it wants to get someplace.

Thursday, August 3, 1944

Got out some of my writing and looked it over. Sometimes, when considering other good writing, and then thinking about how prolific many good writers are, I almost get discouraged. But then they work hard, have plenty of disappointments—and so, if I really want to, I am sure I can equal any writing there is in existence today. The basic requirement is work, and plenty of it. It is time I realized that writing is not pure amusement, but a job as hard and at times more nerve-wracking than many other jobs.

CHAPTER 10

Love, Friendship & Family

Friday, January 22, 1943

I've got a pocket edition of How To Win Friends and Influence People *in my pocket, and am going after it to re-study its contents in a serious manner. There is no doubt that I need to. Glancing through it this evening, I ran upon sections stating: "Be a good listener. Encourage others to talk about themselves ... Talk in terms of the other man's interest ... Make the other person feel important—and do it sincerely."* [7] *This is especially what I need to study upon, as I'm sure I talk less in terms of the other man's interest than in my own. I do so want to make a good and lasting impression on people, and be able to win friends easily.*

And if I can only get out more and associate with people, girls and fellows, and attend social functions more often! These I am sure will [not only] help me from a mental standpoint, but will aid me in my course of studying, influencing, and getting along with people, which I surely wish to improve upon.

Saturday, January 23, 1943

Douglas is sitting on the floor playing with pails and bottles. I just said, "Douglas—hello, honey," and he looked up, smiled, and rattled, "Bo'le,

---

[7] Carnegie, Dale, *How to Win Friends and Influence People.* New York: Simon & Schuster, 1937.

bo'le, de bo'le," which, freely transcribed, means, "Look, here's a bottle, a bottle, a pretty bottle." I surely do love him. It has done me a world of good having a little brother, having to watch after him, and teach and be around him ... Douglas just came out and handed me a jar that he was playing with. As he went back into the front room, I waved to him, and he said, "Bai, bai" (Bye-bye).

Sunday, January 31, 1943

I've sure got to watch myself in conversation. I notice that, unless I restrain myself, all my conversation centers pretty well around my own person, which, in violation of all rules of inter-social volition, will not help my "Winning Friends and Influencing People."

Monday, February 1, 1943

I do hope I can stay well, and keep up my associations with people, and continue on with my few social activities, such as going to church, and especially making more friends. I must try hard to be a good conversationalist, to be friendly, and to be likable. If I can do all of this, then I am sure that I will not have much trouble in increasing my social contacts. But that is not going to be easy.

Friday, February 5, 1943

I really am afraid that I have not got a very good personality. I don't know what makes me think that. I just wonder what other people think of me, and how they think my actions are: conceited, foolish, all right, or what.

Ralph often attended the Mutual meetings organized for teens by the LDS church. He treasured these times when he felt well enough to go out and could socialize with other teens.

Although in his journal, he privately doubted his suitability as a life companion for any of the young women he met, it's clear that Ralph was well-liked, popular, gregarious, and probably outspoken. Although he seems to have felt that his differences made him less attractive to others, it's probable that his mysterious illness made him even more appealing. Since Ralph mentions many friends who are now untraceable, I've often deleted last names.

Sunday, February 7, 1943

They (the girls assembled, must I say) sang for a while, and then when the group sat down, we had various people read from a very good book for about an hour and a half: Added Upon, *by Mr. Nephi Anderson … The majority of these people I did not know before tonight, and I surely did enjoy meeting them, especially Peggy and Ruth—perhaps because I got a little more acquainted with them. After some refreshments and a small discussion, the meeting broke up, but I stayed over for almost forty-five minutes more, talking mostly to Ruth (shame on me!) … Darn, I need to get a method to remember names and faces better!*

Saturday, February 13, 1943

Lucie and I were talking about everything from marriage to people, work, and professions. I do enjoy talking to her. She is a very intelligent conversationalist …

Asked [Lucie] about my actions; and she said it was just the way I talked, my inflection and gestures, that give the idea that I am conceited more than any words that I use. And also that I dominate the scene too much. I will have to purposely restrain myself and analyze my actions in the future, and keep it up until I have changed myself enough so as not to require reconciliations and explanations.

Tuesday, February 16, 1943

I only hope, before I close this account, that I will be in good enough health tomorrow and after to take part in social affairs, and that I will have sense enough to refrain from doing more than what I am capable of. Mother told me last night that whatever I do, never to act disrespectful to my parents in company. Evidently she saw a fellow doing just that yesterday, and it angered her, and built up her dislike for him [so much] that she felt it would be a good thing to tell us to not make a similar mistake, for the sake of others' opinions. Of course, I do not think that we are disrespectful of our parents, but we are on more equal terms with them than are a lot of people; and our familiarity might surprise and perhaps shock others, so we will have to watch ourselves. Too, I have got to watch about talking too much about myself, dominating the scene, and monopolizing conversation, especially in the company of elders; and showing any airs that might be taken to mean conceit. I am told that I do have an air about me, unintentional it must be, that gives others a bad impression of me sometimes; I will have to combat it.

Wednesday, February 17, 1943

Peggy is a very pretty girl (about a year older than myself, I think), and I think she is quite a swell kid, too, as much of her as I know or have observed. I will perhaps see her at the hospital (where she works) Friday when I go to have my blood tested. Also, she would not believe, when I told her, that I had recently been sick, and still do not feel very well. Is it because I look well? Can my actions and ways cover the fact that I limp (or do I also pretty well cover that fact, too)? I surely hope that I can act pretty normal; but I do not want to act foolishly in order to do so. However, a girl will have to take me as I am, healthy or not.

Thursday, February 18, 1943

Last night in bed I was having a pretty blue streak. I almost was on the verge of deciding to stay around home, and cut my "poor" social contact, and refrain my "foolishness" from losing me any more friends. Oh, well, we all have these blue periods, and I think that sometimes they do a person good.

You know, I really don't date very much. Of course, the main reason has been my health. But I think in the future, if I am feeling good enough, that I ought to get out and take girls on dates more than I have. In fact, I haven't had what you would call a date for a good three years. It might do me a lot of good mentally to mix more with people. Of course, if my health doesn't permit it, well then I'll just have to let it go. But if I am in good health, there is little excuse—outside of my disinterest.

Wednesday, April 7, 1943

Something has just happened. Mother is going to the hospital! Alta just stopped in with the news; I am in the kitchen and they were in the front room, and just a minute ago, Donna came home and told me that Mother had just received a telephone call and was crying. I don't know what's the matter … Good gosh, my heart is beating like sixty. I hope it's not serious. I asked Alta how she was, and—she won't tell much—she said it all depends on what happens tonight. Oh, I hope with all my heart it's nothing bad.

In fact, Phoebe Rytting had suffered a miscarriage, although she recovered fully.

Sunday, May 16, 1943

I went down to the Ice-Cream Factory, and bought a cone. Saw Ruth there, too, the first time I have seen her since about the twenty-first of March. Also saw Norma (she lives near us, and is quite a swell person), and Betty ... All were a lot of fun to talk with. I stayed there for about forty-five minutes, buying another cone in the meantime. By the way, while I was there, I saw a poor little fellow standing in front of the place, looking in the window and staring at the people buying cones, and so decided to give him a nickel and let him experience for himself what he must have been dreaming about. I got a kick out of it—and a good feeling.

Saturday, June 12, 1943

I just thought that I would put down my attitude about marriage. It is one of the most important, if not the most important, things to take into consideration if one is to make the most of this life. And just that fact bothers me, for the fact that I have not seen yet even one girl who I could feel I would ever marry. Though I am not looking in that direction at present, yet I am on the lookout for someone who might be a suitable partner. I see quite a few cute girls up here, and fewer serious, intelligent ones, but—maybe I am looking for too much—none seem to be of a temperament suited to me; or if they are, they are either too old or young, or married, or both. The kind of girl I envisage for a wife is one of my own religion (that is of primary importance). I would like her to be intelligent, have interests common to mine, and most of all be interesting, have a personality, and be a good kid (by that I mean have some character to her). I don't know if that is too much to want. First I should be sure that I have that much to offer. But unless I can find some person who I know I should want to have for a wife, not for just this life but for all eternity, then I will remain single ... That consideration keeps me from ever showing much interest in so many girls. They just haven't got what I'm looking for. And what is the use of going out with a girl or getting familiar unless she has what you have envisaged? (Though I do not mean that it should keep you from cultivating friendship with those girls.)

Friday, July 23, 1943

I did feel kind of blue after I got home last night. I just am too darn afraid that I have not got in me what it takes to make real friends. I know I can attract them, but can I hold them? It worries me. My blues have disappeared this morning, though.

CHAPTER 11

Humor

Ralph (left) poses with members of his quartet, which included his best friend Ardean Watts (right), 1944 (see The Arts, page 95)

Monday, January 25, 1943

In the show last night, just to have some fun, I held Jean's hand. It's the devil in me, I'm afraid. I just get these spells now and then. It might be fun to get them more often.

Saturday, January 30, 1943

Tomorrow I'll have to hold a lot of people's hands, kiss a lot of girls, and make love to a dozen more, and maybe I can spice up this narrative. It needs it.

Saturday, February 6, 1943

Well, enough for now (I am afraid I use that phrase too much). Since I have no philosophizing to do, there is no need of my writing at great length. After all, I intend to peruse this sometime in the distant future, and I do not want to be unduly bored with the account.

Thursday, February 11, 1943

I surely do want a family of my own. Though I doubt if any girl would ever have me for a husband: Yeah, me—a wonderful conglomeration of theorizing, speculating, poor health, bad manner, and no S.A. [sex appeal]!

Sunday, June 6, 1943

After some of the folks came back, Lorry and I went outside and looked at the heavens with the telescope. For the first time in my life, I actually saw the moon as a body—its plains, valleys, mountains, craters. It was a thrill. We looked around for Saturn, to see it rings, but could not find it. When Jean happened to come home with a visiting cousin, we showed them the moon. Really kidded them. I told them I just loved to look at "heavenly bodies."

Wednesday, June 9, 1943

In the morning I am destined for a blood transfusion. (It's funny how nonchalantly I wrote that last. I once thought that a transfusion was a great and mysterious operation, given only to the dead or dying. And I really don't feel that far gone.)

Sunday, June 20, 1943

Last night after I had gotten in bed, I heard a scratching noise out in the front room. I soon realized that we had a little mouse visiting us—so I got up and lit out on the warpath. Well, I cornered him in the kitchen cupboard. Then I asked Alta downstairs if she would like to share in a mouse-killing. She asked me where I had him cornered. I told her where, and she burst out laughing. The cupboard I had the mouse "cornered" in was the means of his getting into the house! I was unable to locate him, so I went to bed again. In another half hour, however, the scratching resumed, and I was up until twelve-thirty this time, trying to kill him. My success was very poor. I didn't even catch sight of him the second time.

Saturday, June 26, 1943

I came in around five forty-five, and Donna was making a cake. Then I got the notion into my head that I wanted to make a cake—and nobody could talk me out of it, although they did their darndest. It took me until eight-thirty to get it finished—baked, cooled, and iced. And it really turned out good. I gave everybody in the neighborhood a piece.

Tuesday, June 29, 1943

My ankle is still awfully sore today. It is not a joint hemorrhage, but just a bad bruise on the inside. I'm darned if I know where I got it. Anyway, it is starting to turn all the colors of the rainbow. In that respect, I'm a pretty colorful personality.

Monday, July 5, 1943

I know that my ankle feels better today. I can tell by how it feels tonight. And the swelling is letting up. I said last night that I'd be bowled over if it did start getting better today. "Well, call me ten pins and maul me with a ball!"

Friday, July 16, 1943

I left for the dance, stopping at the Ice-Cream Factory for a cone. I got over to the First Ward Hall at the very beginning of the dance. In fact, I was almost the first one there. I happened to see LaMarr, Keith, and Ralph there. I really enjoyed myself. Danced with a lot of girls, even though I didn't have a partner. As I explained, I didn't have a car to take one in, didn't have the money to hire a taxi, couldn't walk the distance, and didn't have the nerve to ask them to ride on my bicycle. And so—I went "stag."

I came home, and got in bed soon after having a piece of cherry pie. And then I really slept good. And dreamt, too. I was really amorous in my sleep. My subconscious mind really surprises me at times, and shocks me, too. But doesn't overly shock me. My subconscious is me, you see, and I can't very well shock myself—or can I?

Thursday, July 22, 1943

A salesman called at the door, wanting to sell a subscription to The Household Magazine, *which we already take. A free book was also offered with the subscription. Donna answered the door, and after a while she came back with a receipt for the subscription and the free cookbook. She must have thought the salesman had left, for she said, "He just handed me this, and said 'Don't you want the book?'" We thought she had been high-pressured into buying it. Then we started kidding and joking about it. Mother even mentioned in jest the case of the traveling salesman and the farmer's daughter. Little did we know that the salesman was still at the front door, and was hearing everything we said. Well, when we found that out, he was pretty burnt up, I guess, and took the book and left directly. We could hardly contain ourselves, then. We kept laughing about it all day.*

Sunday, August 1, 1943

A little boy was out one day in an orchard, and happened to find a peach-stone. He asked a fellow nearby what it was, and the fellow said that it was a baby seed. If he would plant it in the ground, a baby would grow. Well the little boy planted it in the far corner of the lot, and watered it carefully each day. He even put a tin can over it to mark the spot so he wouldn't lose it. One morning, he went out bright and early to look at it, and when he lifted the can there sat a fat ugly old toad. The boy's face showed astonishment, then despair, and then interest. "Gee," he said, "but you're ugly. If I wasn't your father, I think I'd kill you."

Tuesday, August 17, 1943

Last period of the day, journalism, is going to be swell, even though at first it will be the toughest one of the bunch. We are going to do a year's work in six weeks (or so the teacher tells us), and spend the rest of the year putting out the school paper. There are seventeen in the class, all girls except one other fellow and myself—yippee!

Friday, May 12, 1944

Last night in fun on my [hospital] menu card, I wrote that I wanted Jell-O for breakfast, dinner, and supper. And darned if I didn't have it three times today.

Wednesday, July 5, 1944

I had an extra bit of fun today. Pete bought some mousetraps, and I confiscated one of them, drilled a hole through the bottom of it, put a string through the hole, and fixed it so I could set it off at ease. Then I nailed it to the wall in the back of the shoe department [where Pete works]. Beside the string I put a sign saying: "Do you want to get a bang out of life? Pull string!"

CHAPTER 12

Hope

Thursday, February 25, 1943

Oh, how much like old times it seemed to be out bicycle riding—how good to be able to do the things that I have dreamed about doing for the past two and one-half years ... And I think that my mental attitude is improving right along, too.

Sunday, February 28, 1943

Have just finished a busy, happy day, one of the many which I have been enjoying so much recently. I tell you, health, though not perhaps your most priceless possession, is the nearest thing to it—character (spiritual as well as temporal) being first on the list.

Thursday, May 13, 1943

Have had a thrilling day, both in what I have seen and the wonderful health which I am experiencing. With truth, I can say that I am feeling better right now than I did even at my best last February. I don't know how long it will last, but I am enjoying it with all my heart while I have it.

And man! *Over five hundred cute girls out on the field in attractive white shorts and shirts! That is something I doubt if I'll ever see again—or if I do, it will be a long time from now.*

Friday, June 18, 1943

This has actually been the most active day in years ... The results of my exertions may be a real stiffness tomorrow, or even a slight hemorrhage in some joint. But nonetheless I will be repaid by the wonderful time I have had.

Saturday, June 19, 1943

My big day yesterday has rendered me quite stiff, and made one knee—my left this time—swell. I have very sore soles on my feet, too. But really, all this doesn't begin to offset the good time I had last night. I can hardly wait until I date again. I didn't realize how much I have been missing—though not voluntarily.

Tuesday, July 27, 1943

You know, as I have heard one man say, you can look at the earth and profess atheism, but no true man can look at the heavens and their scintillating light and say with truth that there is no God.

Tuesday, May 16, 1944

Well, today has been quite unusual in several respects. First, I was more active than I ever thought I could be; and second, I attended my own graduation tonight, when all day such a thought was the remotest thing from my mind.

I got up this morning about nine o'clock, and after getting washed up, slid out into the front room and sat in the easy chair for quite a while ... I finished writing yesterday's journal entry and addressed a lot of commencement cards. It was surprising how sleepy I became all of a sudden then. Before I dozed off on the davenport, I did have some good dinner, including some fish Mrs. Watts sent over. I did sleep then, while Mother went downtown and Dad was out in the backyard taking care of Douglas. And I didn't wake up until about four o'clock. I sat then and talked to Dad, who came in the house about that time. I seemed to have an upset stomach, and though it didn't make me sick, I really wasn't very comfortable. I got better soon.

When Mother came home this evening, she mentioned to me that I might be able to go to my graduation tonight, if I'd let Ardean and Dad carry me in. At first I didn't even consider it. Then I let them try to carry me over to the piano bench to see if it could be done—and I sat there for about twenty minutes and played the piano. It seemed so good, I didn't know what to think. Well, finally I decided to go tonight. There was a risk involved, but I felt it would be worth it. So I got all slicked up and dressed in my brown suit.

Dad and Ardean carried me out to Watts' car, and we rode over to the Junior High, where the commencement exercises were being held. Well, they carried me in amidst the crowd, and I have to admit I felt self-conscious—but then who wouldn't? And I was so thrilled by the wonderful way kids came up to talk to me, and how thrilled they seemed to see me out. Worge, Trixie, Dude, Merrilyn, and even Mr. Crowley came over and talked to me. I was given a cap and gown, too. Then the exercises started, and they were lovely. Two hundred and thirty-three seniors graduated—and to think that I was fifth highest in the class! The services were fairly long, but I enjoyed them. And after they were over and I had my diploma, everyone congratulated me. Anita came over, too, and we were both so thrilled we hardly knew what to do. She was surprised to see me, too. We visited and compared grades. We're about even. I have twenty-four A's and eleven B's for four years. And that's pretty good. No C's, thank you. I left for home then, with Dad's and Ardean's assistance. After getting home, I sat and visited for a while with the family. I got to bed directly, but because I was so excited, it was hours before I could get to sleep.

Friday, May 26, 1944

And sensing the utter beauty and peacefulness of this day, it is hard to believe that it is not the same elsewhere. Yet at this very moment, as I write these few lines, war—in all its full and terrible fury—is being waged. I'm thankful to be here.

ACKNOWLEDGMENTS

I would like to recognize Specialty Therapeutic Care for generously sponsoring this edition of the book. Thank you for providing outstanding support to the hemophilia community and for your mission to provide collaborative services by putting patients at the center of your work.

I cannot thank Gavon and Tanya Barkdull, Dallin and Natalie Wright, and Matt and Rebecca Dalsing enough. I value your love and generosity! I also wish to extend great appreciation to Ardean Watts, my grandfather's lifelong friend, who provided invaluable insight. In addition, this book could never have been launched without the resource of Ralph's precious journals, made available by my mother, Elizabeth Rytting Barkdull, and my grandmother, the late Georgia Shaw. The degree to which they helped is incalculable.

Special credit goes to my father, Larry Barkdull, for his editorial suggestions and constant encouragement. And to Colby Rytting, Ralph's son, who had a tremendous impact on this project by giving me perspective regarding the context of Ralph's words.

To the professional team at Eschler Editing and Scrivener Books: thank you! Their creativity and dedication made this edition of the book even better than what I'd previously imagined! And to my good friends at LA Kelley Communications—including Laurie Kelley and Tracy Brody, who published the first edition of Legacy—I offer my gratitude for your vision and giving this book its voice eight years ago.

Finally, I thank my wife, Kristin, for her constant reassurance and support, and for arranging schedules so I could finish this project. Her level of sacrifice was immeasurable.

—Matthew Dean Barkdull
Riverton, Utah
August 2014

ABOUT THE AUTHOR

Matthew Dean Barkdull is a licensed marriage and family therapist and a certified medical family therapist. He is presently in business school working towards his MBA degree. Matt is the proud grandson of Ralph Dean Rytting from whom he inherited severe hemophilia. He has a special interest in helping people that struggle with chronic, terminal, and acute illnesses as Matt himself is a cancer survivor, the recipient of two different kidney transplants after three years on dialysis, and overcoming a severe West Nile viral infection. He loves life and is glad each day to be alive! Matt lives in Utah with his beautiful family consisting of his wife, Kristin, and their three daughters: Makenna, Grace, and Ellen.

Specialty
Therapeutic Care
an AcariaHealth™ company

Made in the USA
Coppell, TX
15 September 2022